Learning to Read with Clues to **Meaning**

C

Ann L. Staman

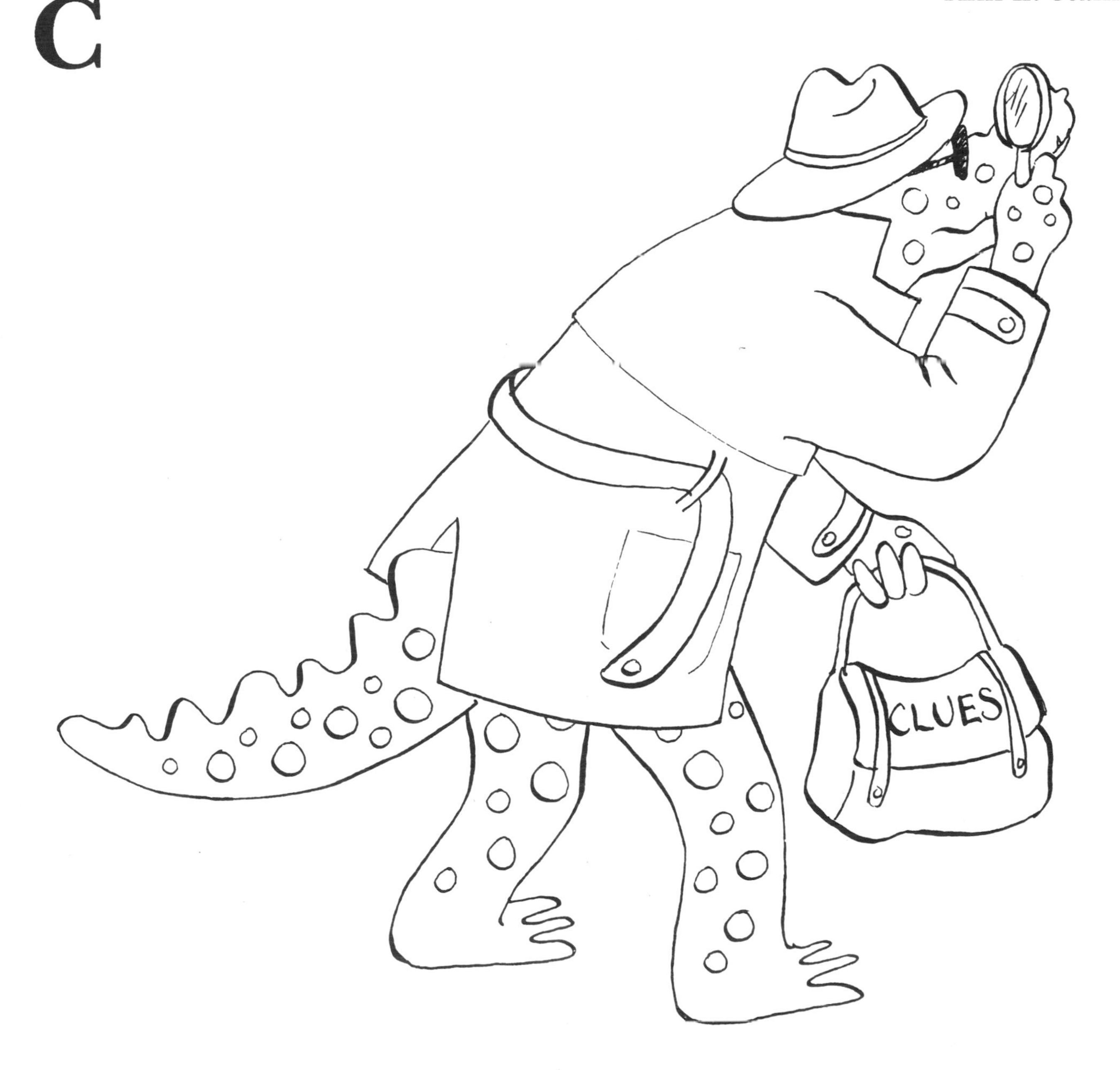

Educators Publishing Service, Inc.
Cambridge and Toronto

To the Teacher

Clues to Meaning is a beginning reading series that treats phonetic decoding as one strategy among many for unlocking meaning from a text. The books encourage readers to use semantic and syntactic clues, as well as sounds, to decipher unknown words. Sound-letter correspondences are introduced through carefully sequenced exercises, designed to invite children to notice the phonemic similarities and differences between words.

After becoming familiar with a sound-letter pattern, students are encouraged to use phonetic strategies in conjunction with pictorial, semantic, and contextual clues as they work with a variety of realistic reading situations. Beginning readers learn to use phonics the way experienced readers do—in a flexible and strategic manner—as they engage in meaningful reading and writing activities.

In This Book

Cover design and text illustrations by Anne Lord

Dedicated to Mary Baltren, who teaches first grade
in Belchertown, Massachusetts.

Thanks to Dorothy Miller
for all her patience, encouragement, and editorial assistance.

 Printed in U.S.A. ISBN 0-8388-2273-8

July 2002 Printing

Hi! We are Fred the Frog and Clem the Clam. If we see a word we can't read, we look for clues.
FISH
Sometimes we look at the picture.
This is a shark.
Sometimes we look at the rest of the sentences.
The shark swims in the ocean.
It has big, sharp teeth.
Sometimes we use words we know.
she
are
park
And sometimes we use the sounds we know. . .

FROGS
CLAMS
We are reading about sound clues right now.
Words can begin with one consonant or **two** — like this:
rip →
drip
and this:
lock →
clock
Let's look at some more of these sound clues . . .

Write: Jessica Salcedo

clam	clap	clock

Picture	Word
(clock)	clock
(clam)	clam
(clap)	clap

flag	floss	flip

Picture	Word
(floss)	floss
(flip)	flip
(flag)	flag

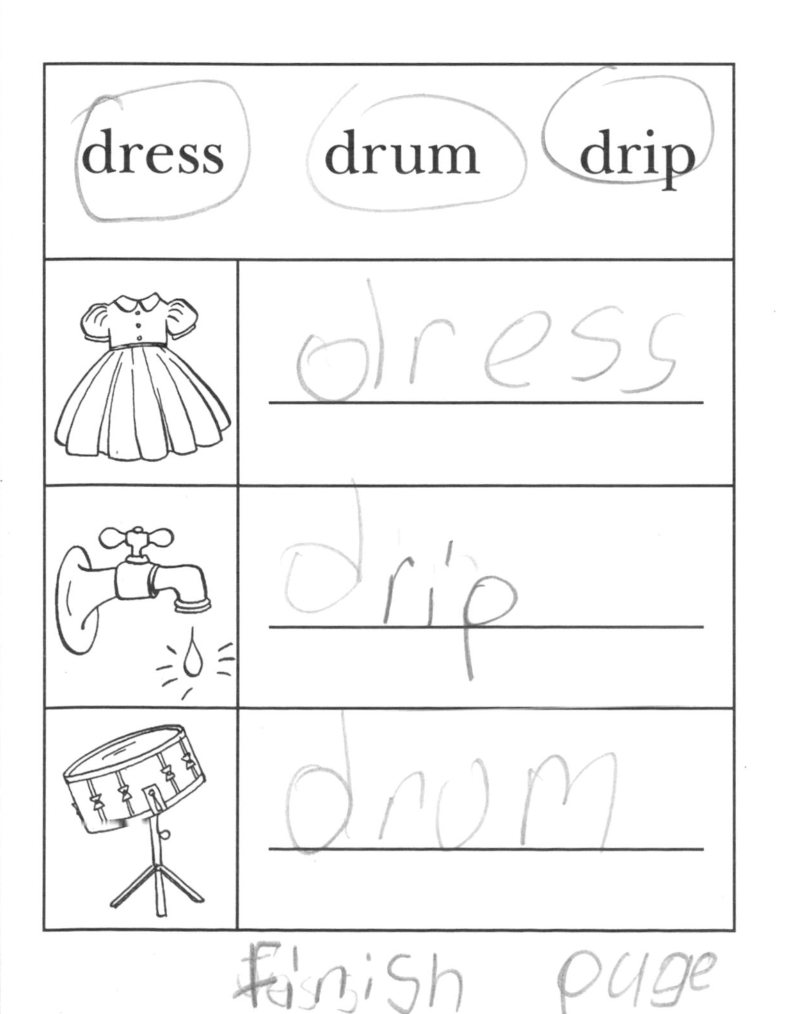

Finish page

Write:

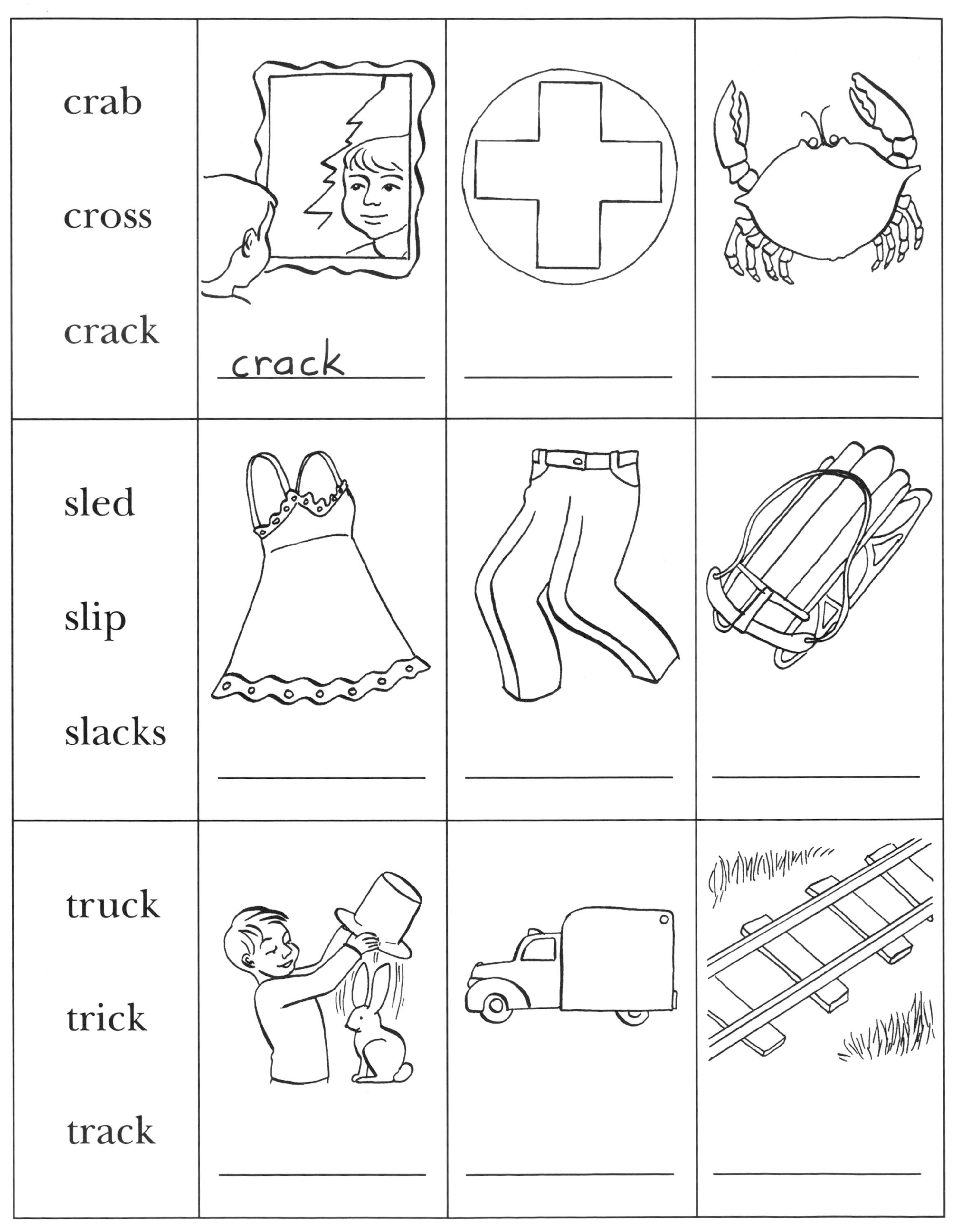

Write:

 ________________	trap
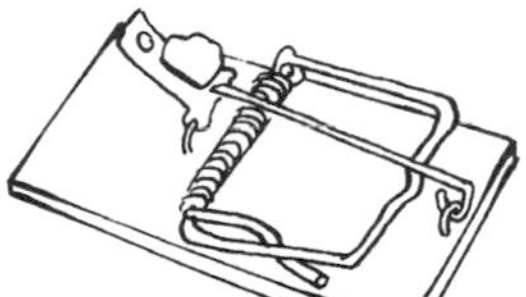 trap	slap
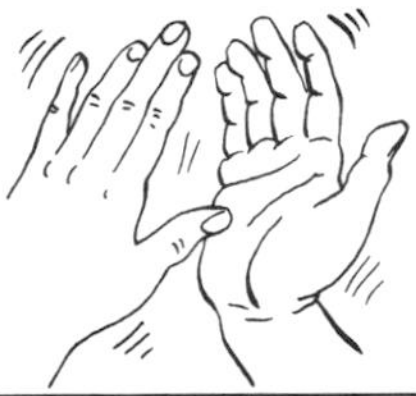 ________________	clap

 ________________	glass
 ________________	grass
 ________________	class

 ________________	black
 ________________	stack
 ________________	crack

clap
clam
laps
cap
Gran
pin
ring
grin
lips
flip
fill
pill
bark
crab
crack
bran
fog
roof
frog
grab
FLOSS
floss
flat
loss
slop
B
J
bull
lock
black
block
prod
drip
drop
trot
grass
glad
lags
glass
drag
drum
dumb
mud
track
trick
crack
cart
2
2
4
plum
slip
plus
sup
brag
click
crack
brick
slacks
crab
cross
class
slip
slid
spill
lips

⬭ and write:

Fran
Fran
clam
slid
brick
plum
block
BLACK
B
press
prrrr
prrrrr

Match and write:

black

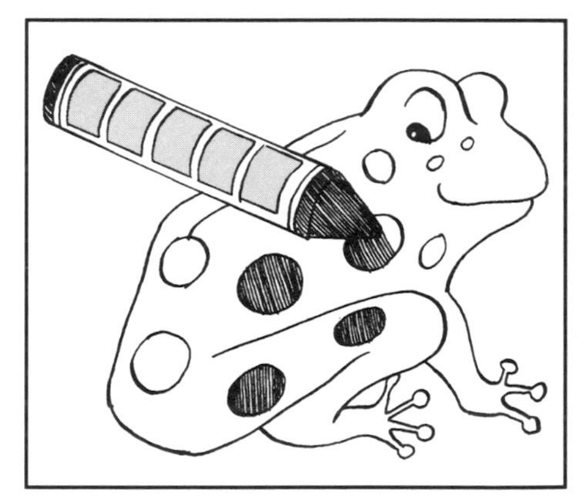

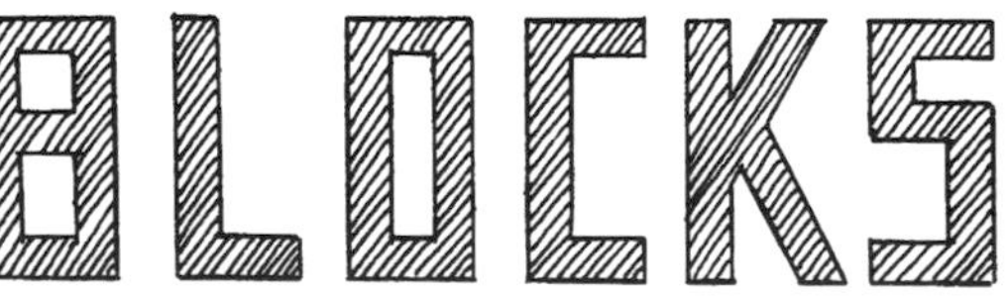

Use the words in the box. Fill in the blanks:

Gran	trap	flag	flat
flip	clap	slip	crib

Brett did a ____.

Let's wave the ____.

The kids ____ for Fran.

She is my ____.

Dad has a ____ tire.

The mouse is in the ____.

The baby has a new ____.

Grace put on the ____.

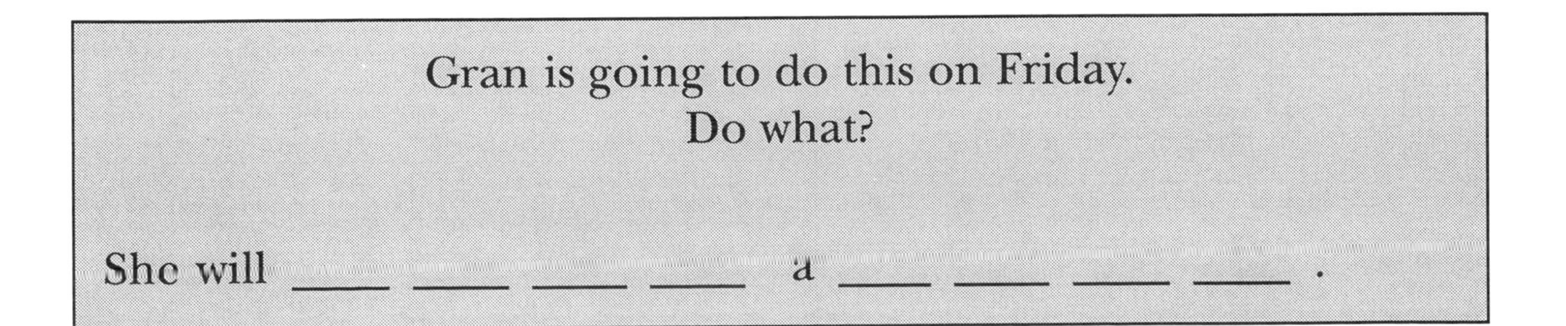

Gran is going to do this on Friday.
Do what?

She will ____ ____ ____ ____ a ____ ____ ____ ____.

Write:

slacks

clam

brat

dress

drum

crab

sled

blocks

frog

slip

X the one that does not belong:

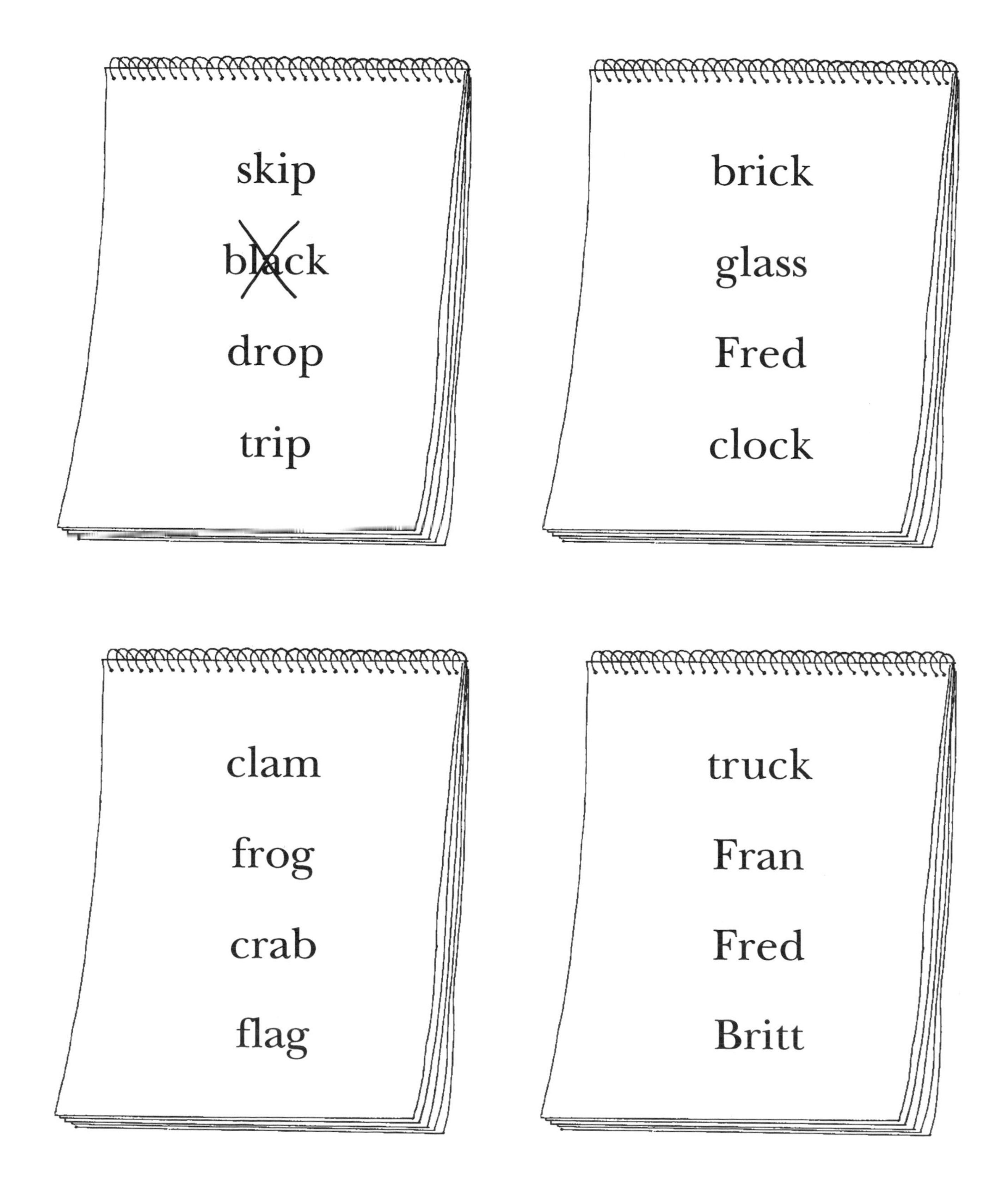

Think about the **sounds**. What word comes next?

brad	brick	brat	bran	trap slid clock grass ~~bran~~
slap	sled	slip	________	
flip	clap	drip	________	
dress	cross	floss	________	

Think about the **meanings**. What word comes next?

Where do these belong?
* = bonus word!

~~dress~~	* blue jeans
grass	frog
slip	* blouse
tree	slide

Write:

Kris is on the sled.

________ is on the trolley.

________ is on the slide.

Clem truck Gran class Fran ~~sled~~

________ is on the train.

Brett is on the ________.

The ________ is on the bus.

Where are you?

I am ________________________.

Cut on dotted lines and fold on solid line. Put together to form booklet. Staple and color.

Clem is dressed up
as a frog.
2
FOLD
Fred's cat is dressed up, too.
7
Brenda is dressed up
as a clown.
4
FOLD
Fran is dressed up
as a bride.
5

I cried when my gran died. When did you cry?
I cried when

Hi! We are Stella the Stork and Skip the Skunk. We are reading about words that begin with 2 consonants instead of 1.
Words can begin with one consonant or two — like this:
win→
twins
and this:
top→
stop
Let's look at some more of these sound clues . . .

Write:

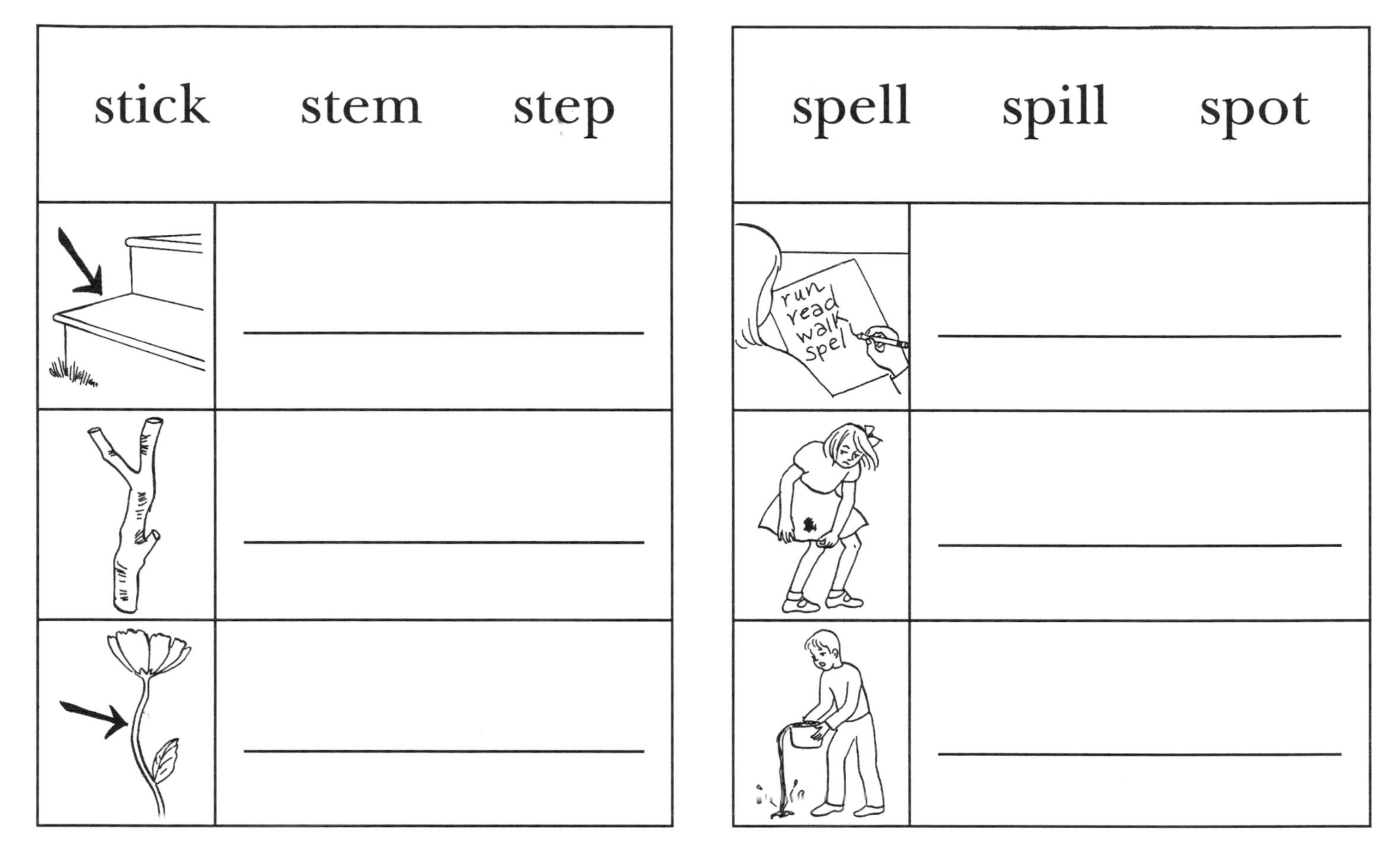
stick stem step
spell spill spot
run
read
walk
spel

skip skin skid

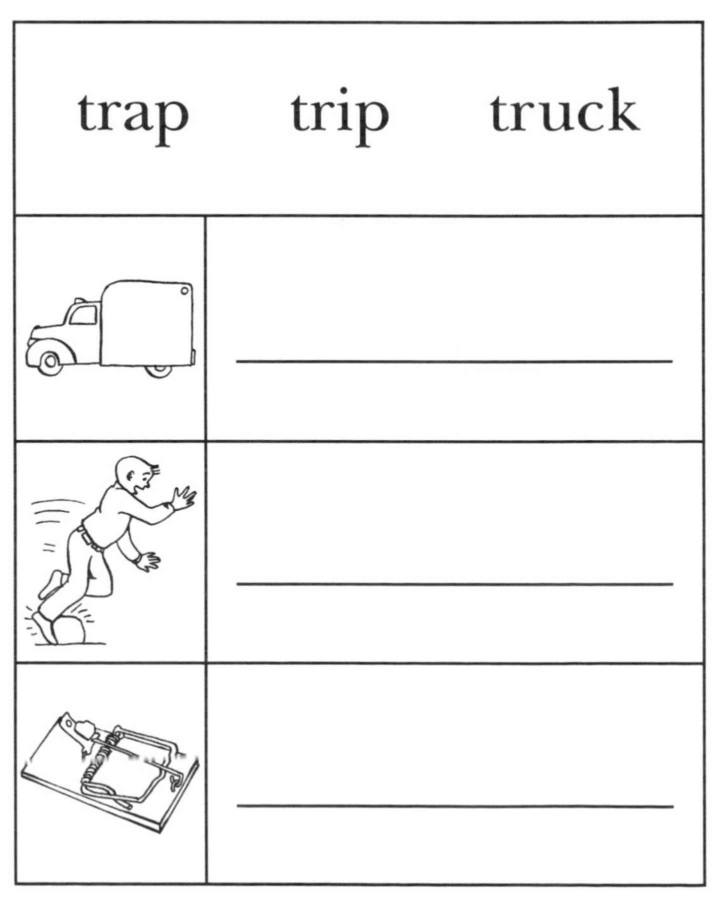
trap trip truck

Write:

Write:

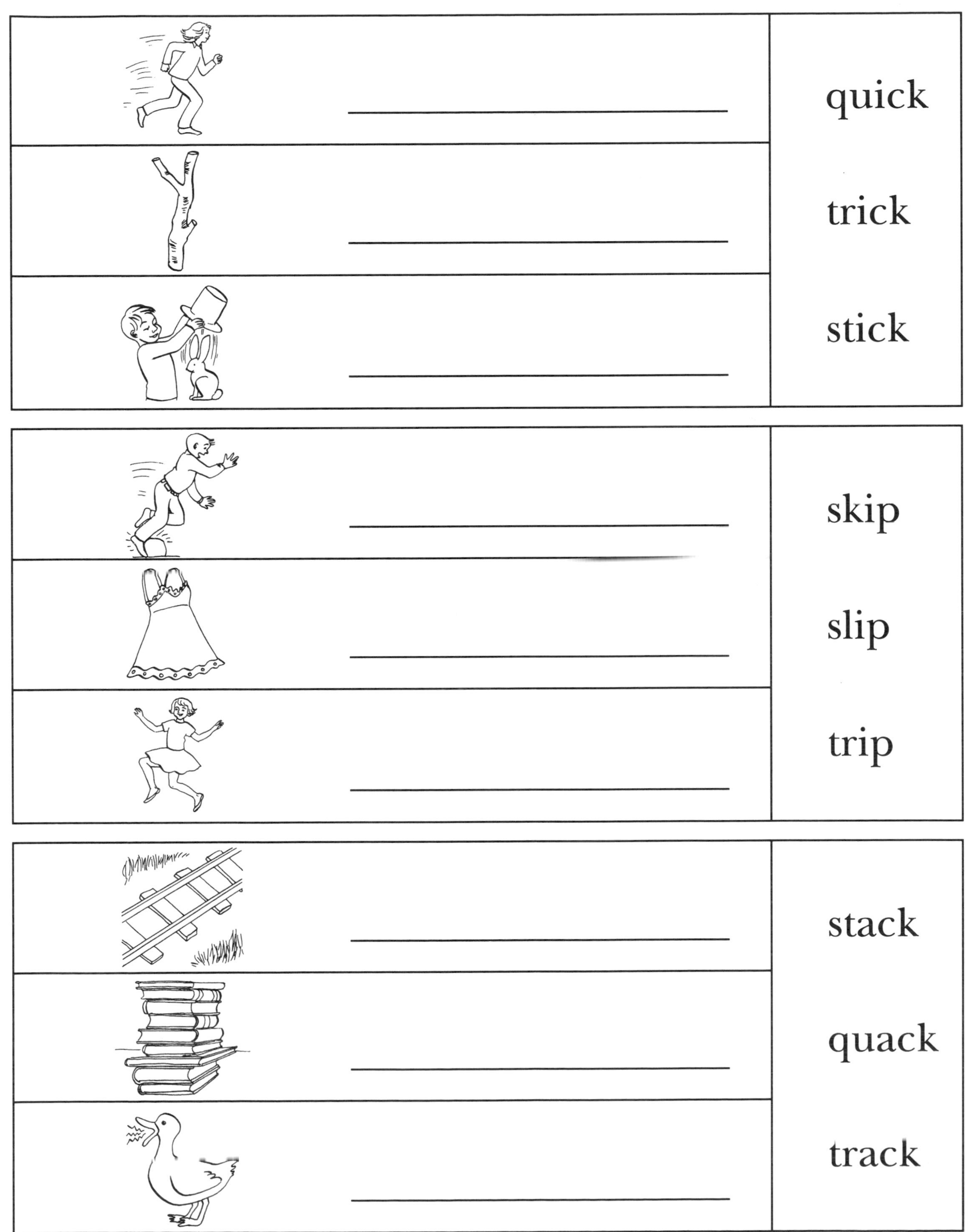

:

spot
stop
pots
step
run
read
walk
spel
spill
slip
spell
lips
trip
swim
newt
twin
slam
small
limps
smell
quiz
quick
quack
kick
skid
kids
skip
dikes
track
trap
trot
spot
cats
stack
stuck
stick
Scott
skit
tacks
scat!
shack
snack
cans
snake
spill
lips
slip
pills
spin
snip
nips
span
smell
comes
skim
smock
truck
track
trick
cart
skim
spin
skin
nicks

◯ and write:

swim
trick
spill
run
read
walk
spel
quit
tick
tick
step
Stella
run
read
walk
spel
skip

Match and write:

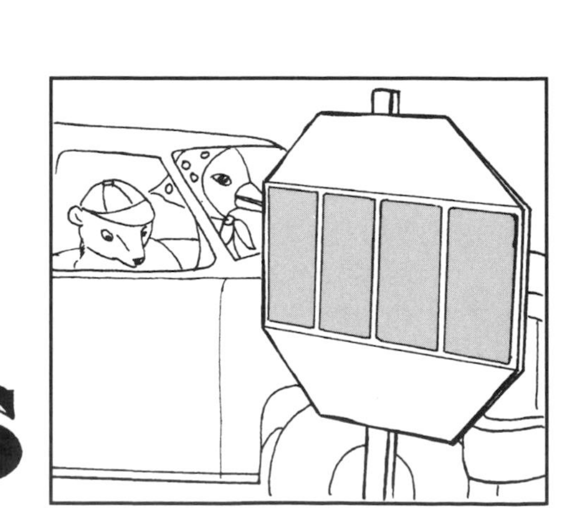

TRUCKS

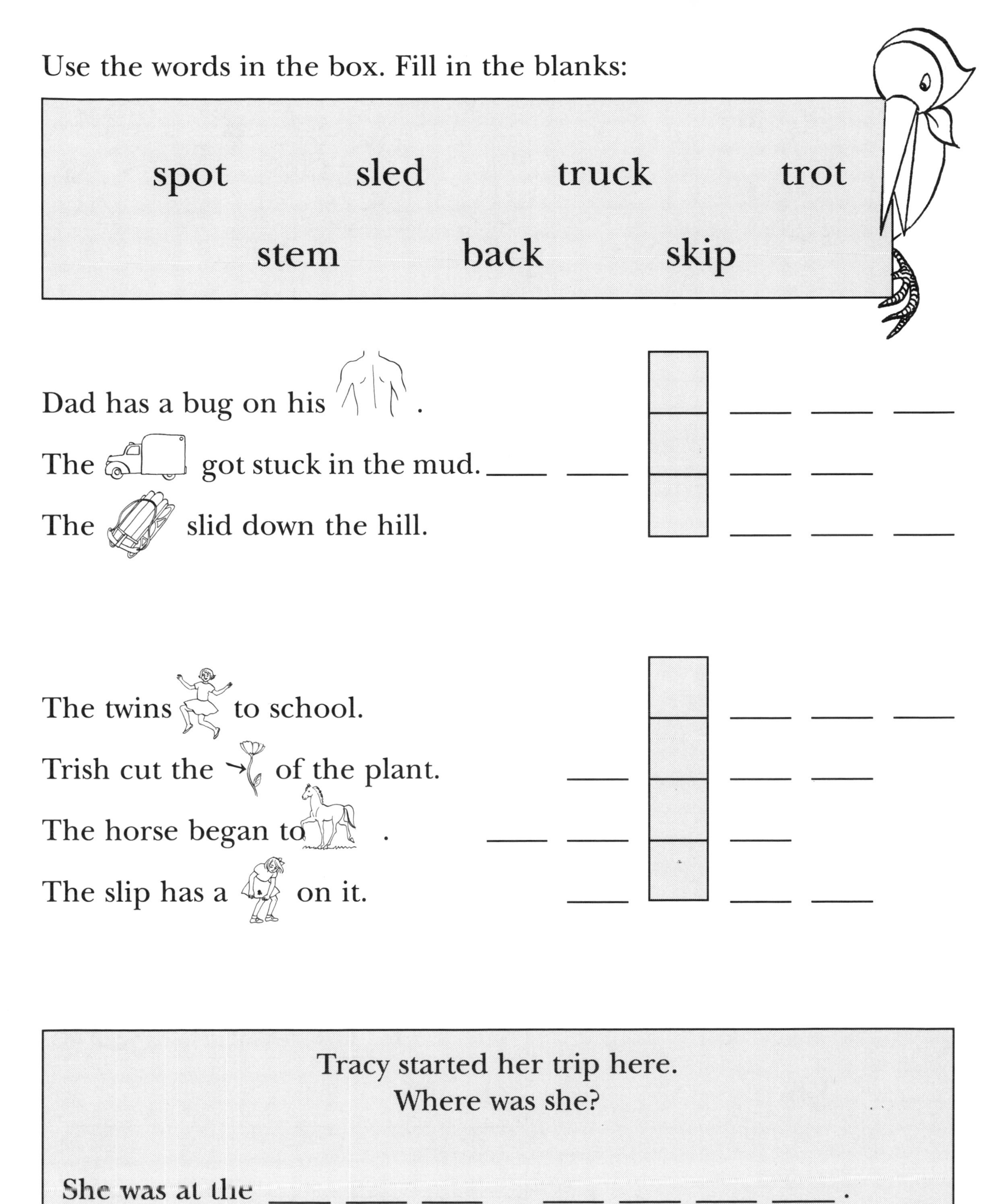
Use the words in the box. Fill in the blanks:

spot sled truck trot
stem back skip

Dad has a bug on his .

The got stuck in the mud.

The slid down the hill.

The twins to school.

Trish cut the of the plant.

The horse began to .

The slip has a on it.

Tracy started her trip here.
Where was she?

She was at the ___ ___ ___ ___ ___ ___ ___.

Write:

Stella

sled

still

smock

slip

trap

dress

stick

Stan

twins

CLOTHES	
1	
2	
3	

PEOPLE	
1	
2	
3	

THINGS	
1	
2	
3	

X the one that does not belong:

Think about the **sounds**. What word comes next?

quick	quiz	quack	______	skip
snug	snip	snob	______	snack
still	smell	spell	______	quit
slip	slap	step	______	trot
				spill

Think about the **meanings**. What word comes next?

Where do these belong?
* = bonus word!

truck	sled
tree	* trail
skunk	grass
* spare tire	bricks

Write:

What do you try to do?

I try to _______________________________ .

Cut on dotted lines and fold on solid line. Put together to form booklet. Staple and color.
Oh-oh! I smell smoke!
8
FOLD
Mmmmm!
1
Mmmm! I smell hot dogs!
6
FOLD
Mmmm! I smell cake!
3

FOLD
Mmmm! I smell pizza!
2
Mmmm! I smell flowers!
7
FOLD
Mmmm! I smell cookies!
4
Mmmm! I smell pancakes!
5

I smile when
I feel happy.
When do you smile?
I smile when

KNOTS
Hi! We are Shelly the Sheep and Chip the Chipmunk. We are reading about **two** consonants that make **one sound** . . .
. . . like this:
ship
thin
and this:
wrap
knot
Let's look at some more of these sound clues . . .

Write:

thick thin them

Write:

Write:

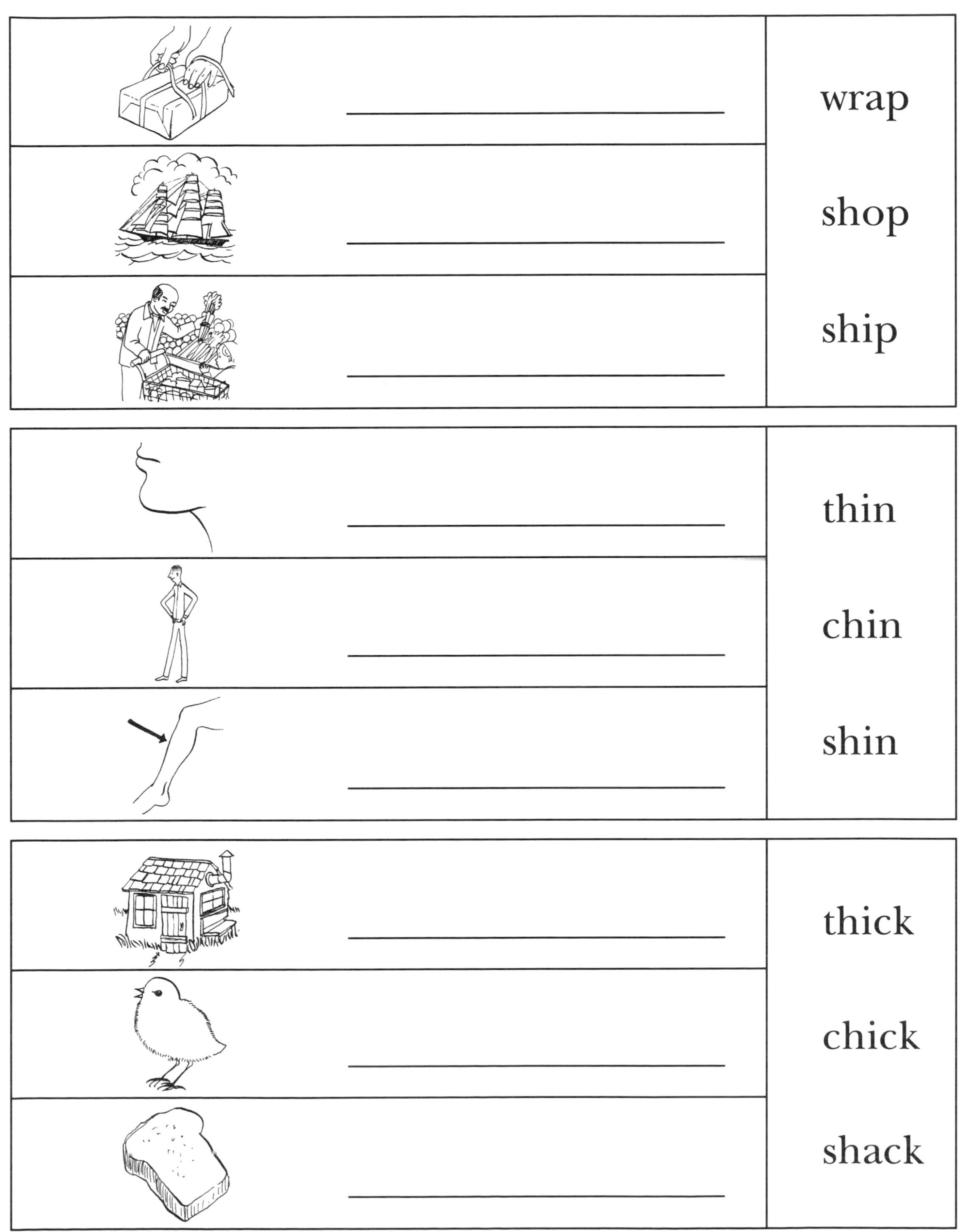

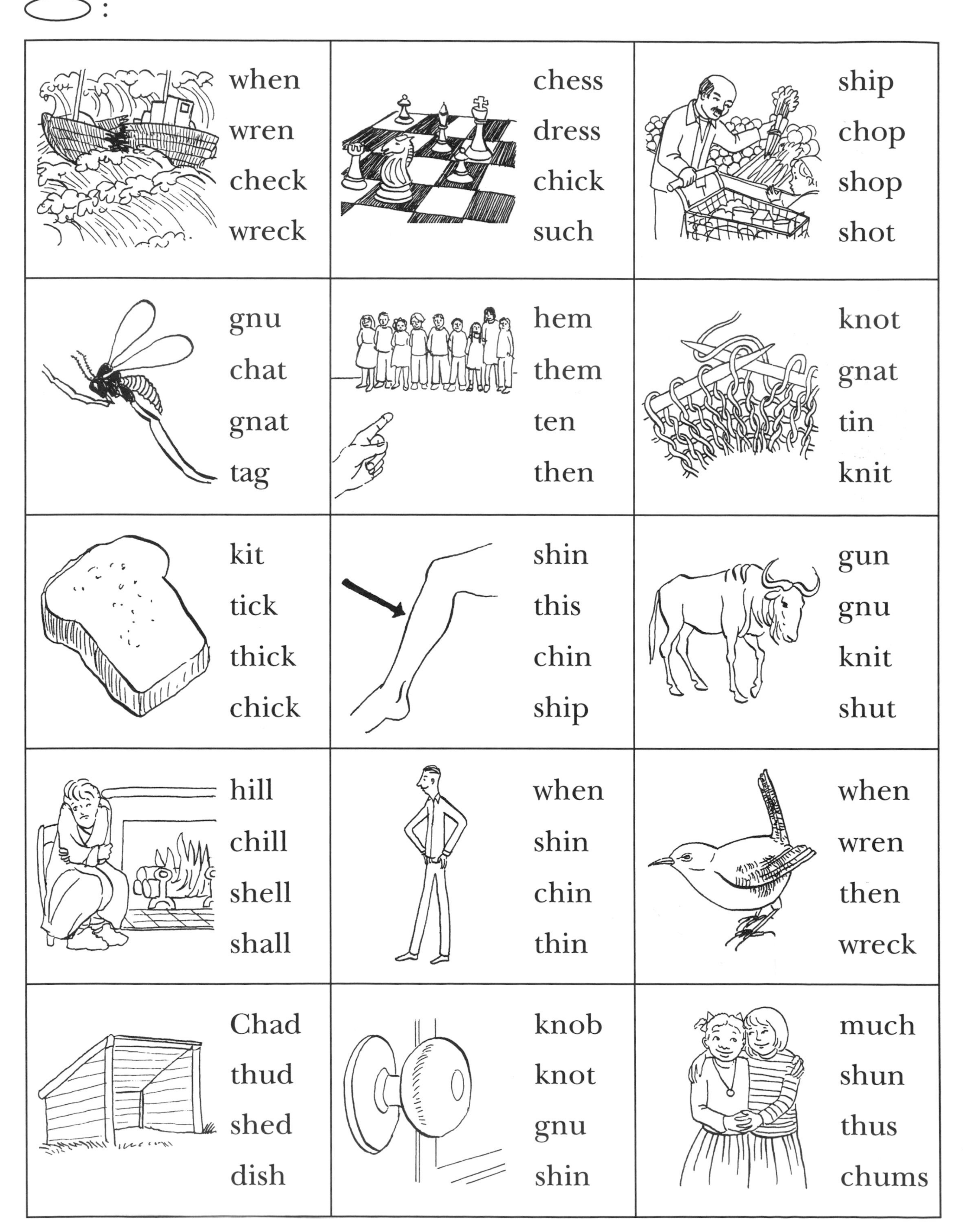
when
wren
check
wreck
chess
dress
chick
such
ship
chop
shop
shot
gnu
chat
gnat
tag
hem
them
ten
then
knot
gnat
tin
knit
kit
tick
thick
chick
shin
this
chin
ship
gun
gnu
knit
shut
hill
chill
shell
shall
when
shin
chin
thin
when
wren
then
wreck
Chad
thud
shed
dish
knob
knot
gnu
shin
much
shun
thus
chums

⬭ and write:

Match and write:

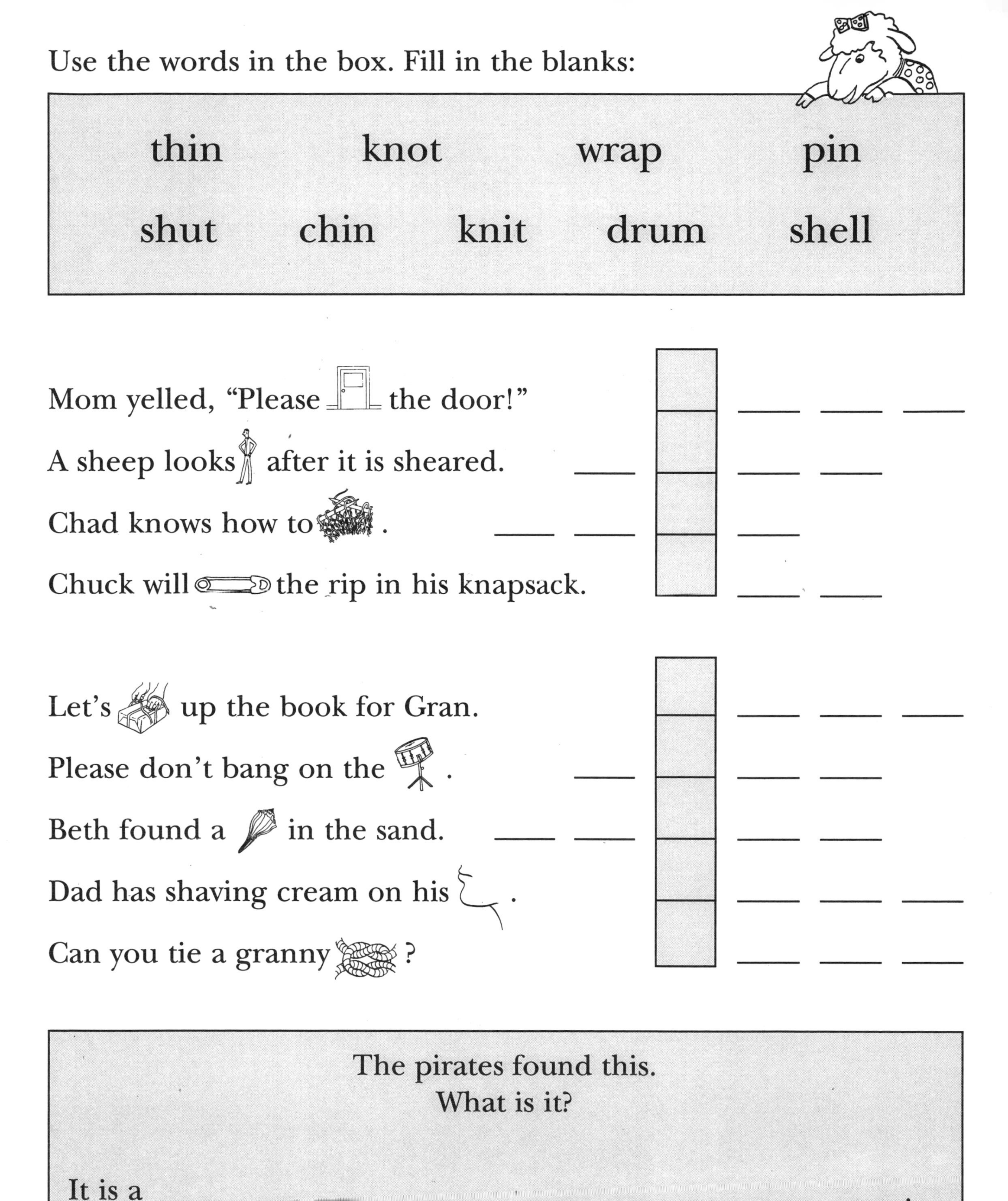

Use the words in the box. Fill in the blanks:

thin	knot	wrap	pin	
shut	chin	knit	drum	shell

Mom yelled, "Please ___ the door!" ___ ___ ___ ___

A sheep looks ___ after it is sheared. ___ ___ ___ ___

Chad knows how to ___ . ___ ___ ___ ___

Chuck will ___ the rip in his knapsack. ___ ___ ___

Let's ___ up the book for Gran. ___ ___ ___ ___

Please don't bang on the ___ . ___ ___ ___ ___

Beth found a ___ in the sand. ___ ___ ___ ___ ___

Dad has shaving cream on his ___ . ___ ___ ___ ___

Can you tie a granny ___ ? ___ ___ ___ ___

The pirates found this.
What is it?

It is a ___ ___ ___ ___ ___ ___ ___ ___ ___ .

Write:

chum

knob

Chet

wren

knot

shell

then

gnu

Shelly

chick

ANIMALS	
1	
2	
3	

PEOPLE	
1	
2	
3	

THINGS	
1	
2	
3	

X the one that does not belong:

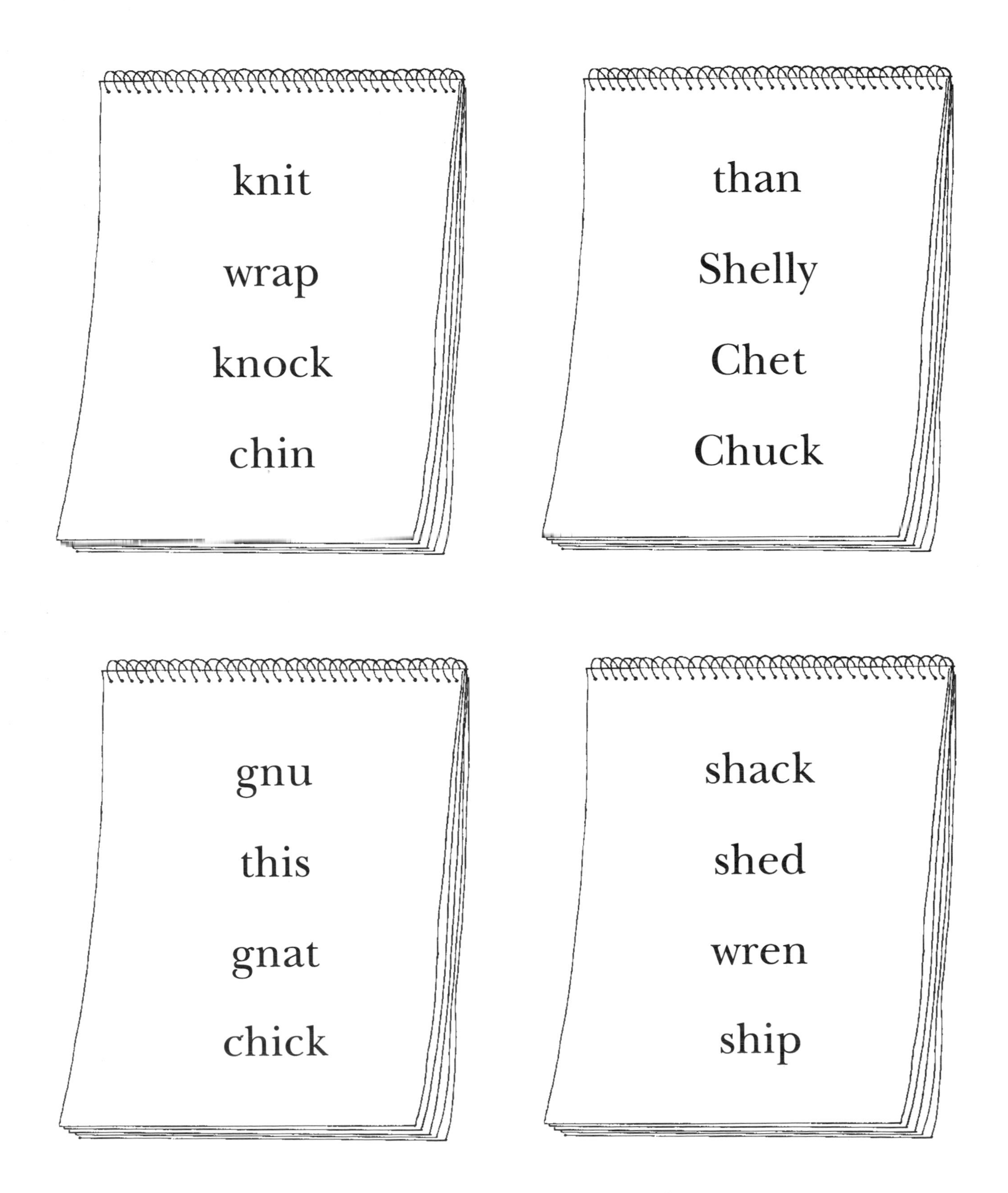

Think about the **sounds**. What word comes next?

then	that	than	____________
whip	wham	whack	____________
wrap	chip	shop	____________
gnat	that	chat	____________

knot

this

when

gnu

ship

Think about the **meanings**. What word comes next?

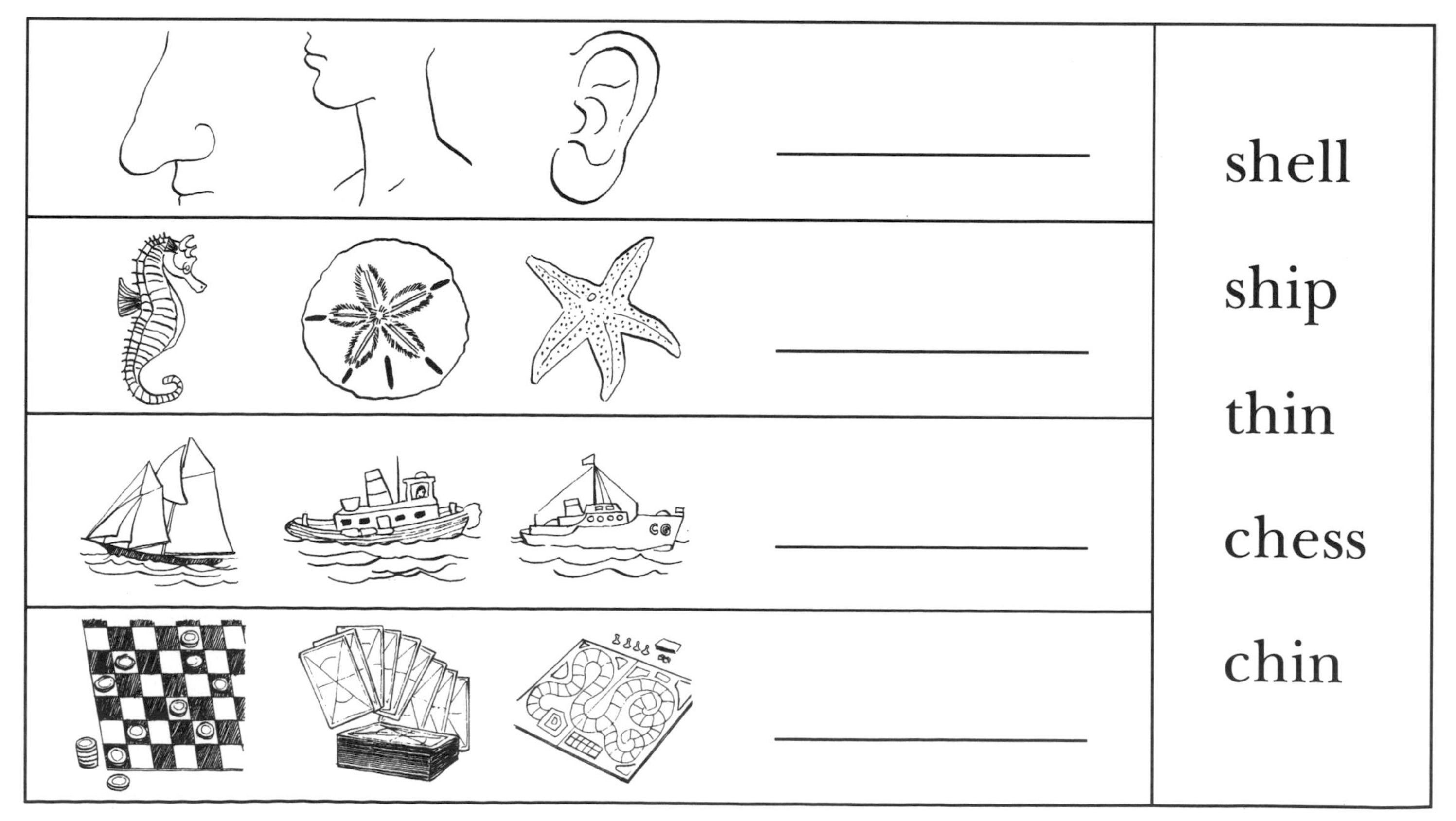

Where do these belong?
∗ = bonus word!

cherries	knife
beach	ship
whale	shell
* chick·en	lamb chop

Write:

Chet shops for ________.

Sharon shops for a ________.

The ________ shops for a chair.

Deb ship chess shells Chad chick

________ shops for shoes.

________ shops for a phone.

Shane shops for a ________ set.

What do **you** shop for?

I shop for ________________________________.

Cut on dotted lines and fold on solid line. Put together to form booklet. Staple and color.

BIGGER

An elephant is bigger than a cat.

1

A chick is bigger than a gnat.

3

A whale is bigger than a gnu.

6

and I am bigger than you!

8

FOLD

FOLD

A phone is bigger than a bell.

2

He is bigger than she,

7

A ship is bigger than a shell.

4

A shin is bigger than a knee.

5

I think it's
wrong to steal.
What do you think
is wrong?

I think it's
wrong to

Hi! We are Wolfgang the Wolf and Trish the Fish. We are reading about words that **end** with two or more consonants . . .
. . . like this:
in
inch

and this:
ten
tent

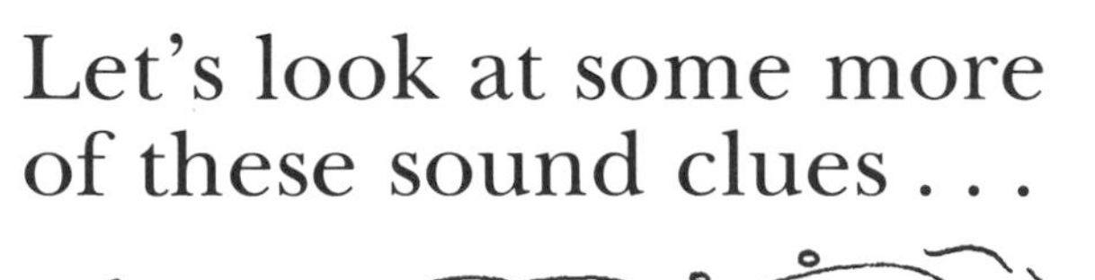
Let's look at some more of these sound clues . . .

Write:

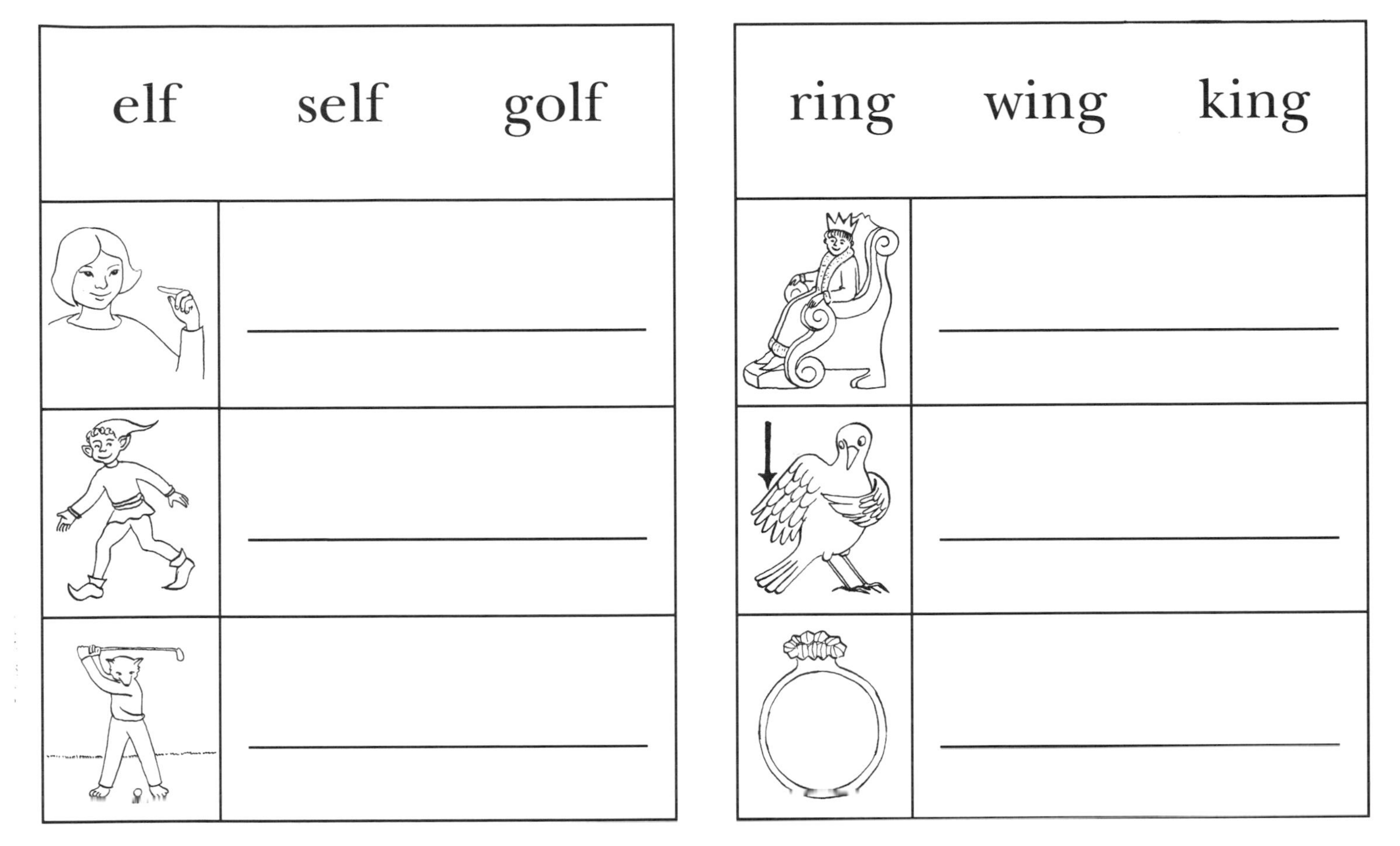

hand band sand

Write:

Words			
match hatch catch	______	______	______
path bath math	______	______	______
wish fish dish	______	______	______

Write:

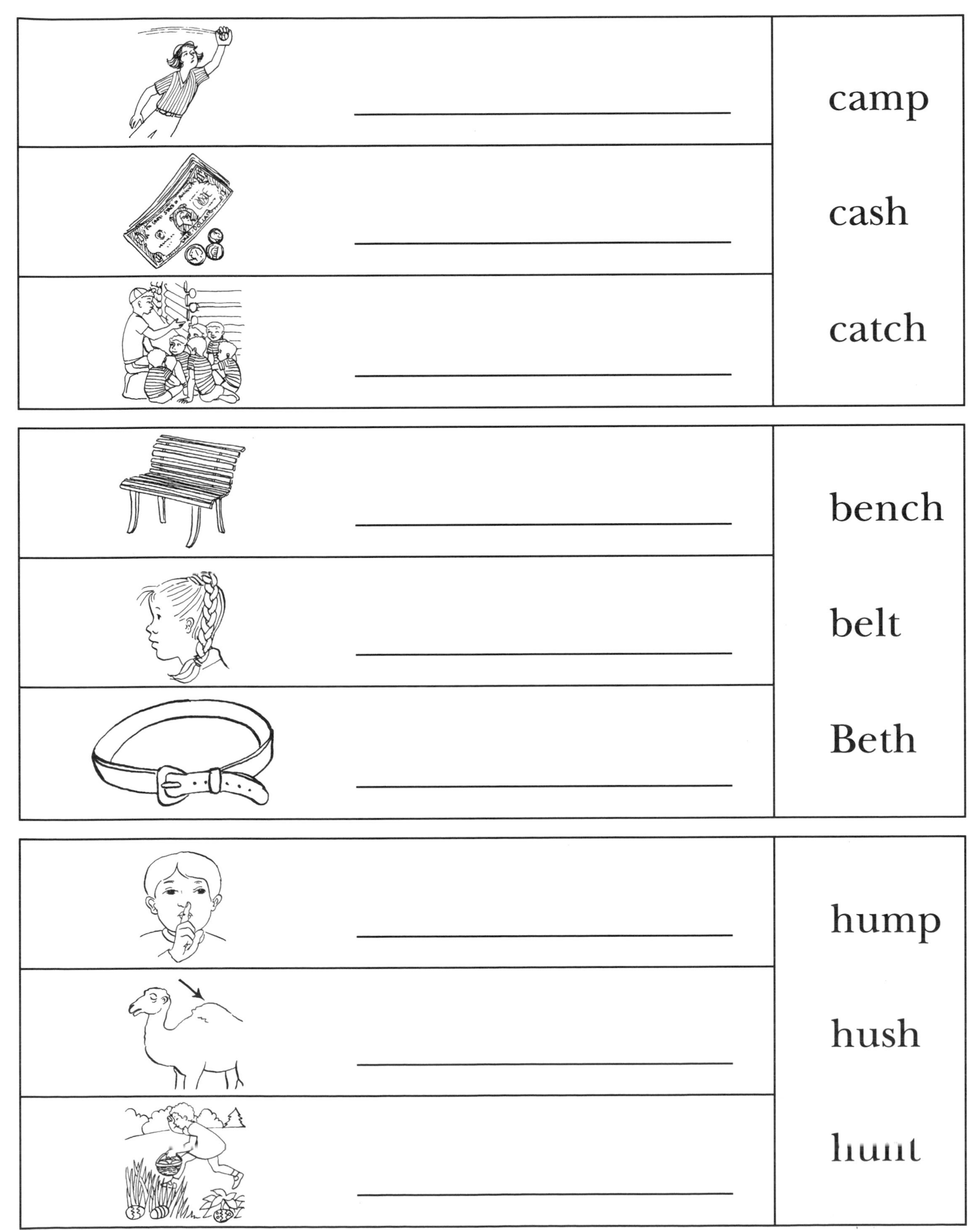

:
limp
land
palm
lamp
golf
gulf
flag
gold
MILK
QUART
mild
silk
Clem
milk
melt
felt
elm
mend
left
lift
felt
list
gulp
help
helm
plan
sing-song
ding-dong
ping-pong
pink
judge
fudge
hutch
gruff
bunch
lung
chill
lunch
elk
elm
end
edge
pitch
chap
match
patch
judge
just
junk
sunk
since
dance
fence
dash
pond
bend
post
dump
mash
math
scam
mask

and write:

ink				
witch				
badge				
fist				
desk				
pants				
bath				

Match and write:

Use the words in the box. Fill in the blanks:

king	inch	song	hand
golf	lamp	wink	hump

That (lamp) has no bulb in it. ___ ___ ___ [ ]

Randy will (wink) at me when he sings. ___ [ ] ___ ___

The elf is just one (inch) tall. ___ [ ] ___ ___

The (king) is very rich. ___ ___ ___ [ ]

That camel has one (hump). ___ ___ ___ [ ]

Mom's (golf) ball went near the pond. ___ [ ] ___ ___

Wendy made a fist with her (hand). ___ ___ [ ] ___

Hank sang a (song). ___ ___ ___ [ ]

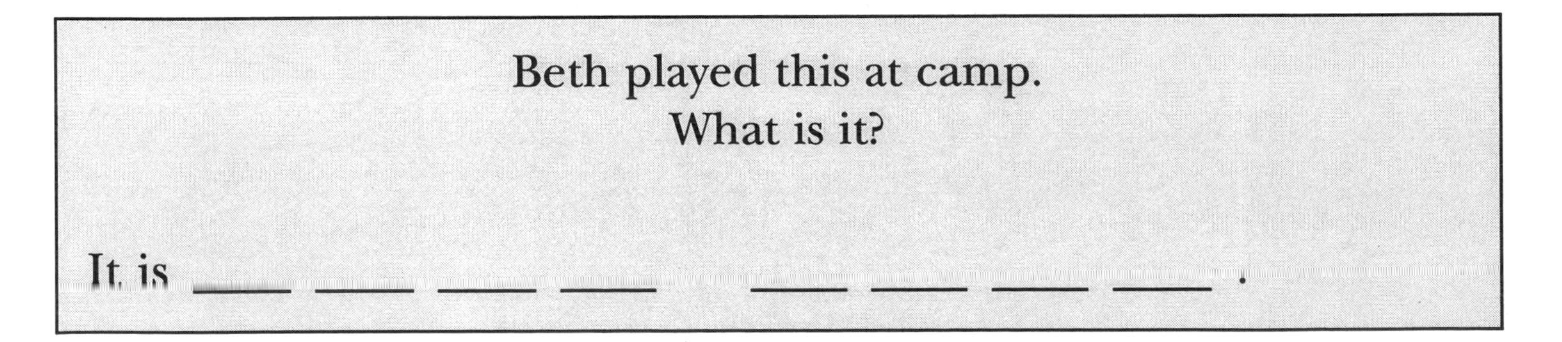

Beth played this at camp.
What is it?

It is ___ ___ ___ ___ ___ ___ ___ ___ .

Write:

vest

lamb

ranch

camp

left

pants

fish

belt

mink

bank

PLACES	
1	
2	
3	

CLOTHES	
1	
2	
3	

ANIMALS	
1	
2	
3	

X the one that does not belong:

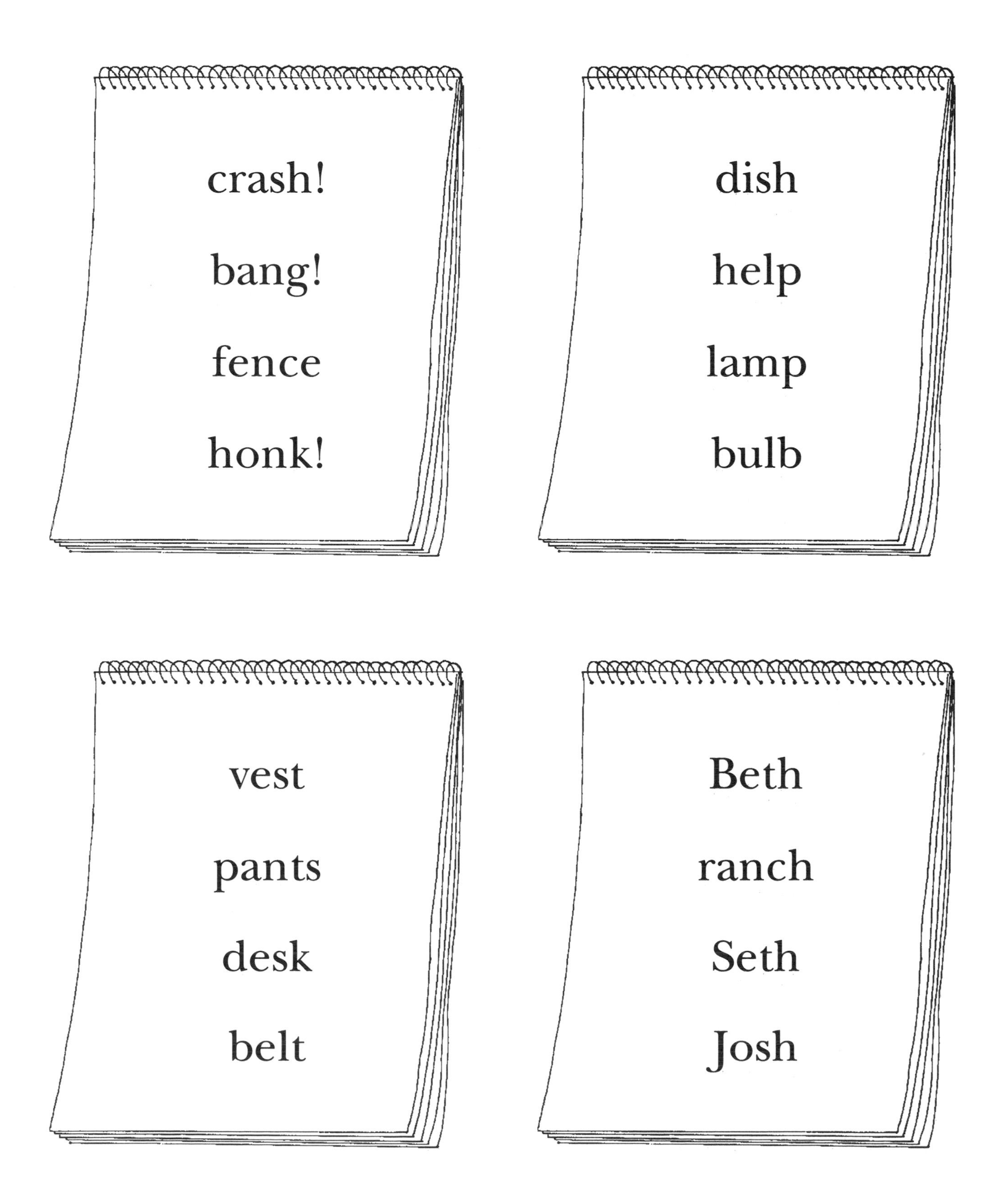

Think about the **sounds**. What word comes next?

raft	rash	rang	______	wing
wilt	wish	witch	______	ramp
mend	send	bend	______	lend
rash	cash	mash	______	dash
				mint

Think about the **meanings**. What word comes next?

Where do these belong?
* = bonus word!

test	raft
desk	pond
bunk bed	tent
* teacher	* math book

Write:

Where did you go?

I went to ____.

Cut on dotted lines and fold on solid line. Put together to form booklet. Staple and color.

FOLD
Catch a cold and rest for a while.
8
Catching
1
FOLD
Catch a cricket.
6
Catch a dish.
3

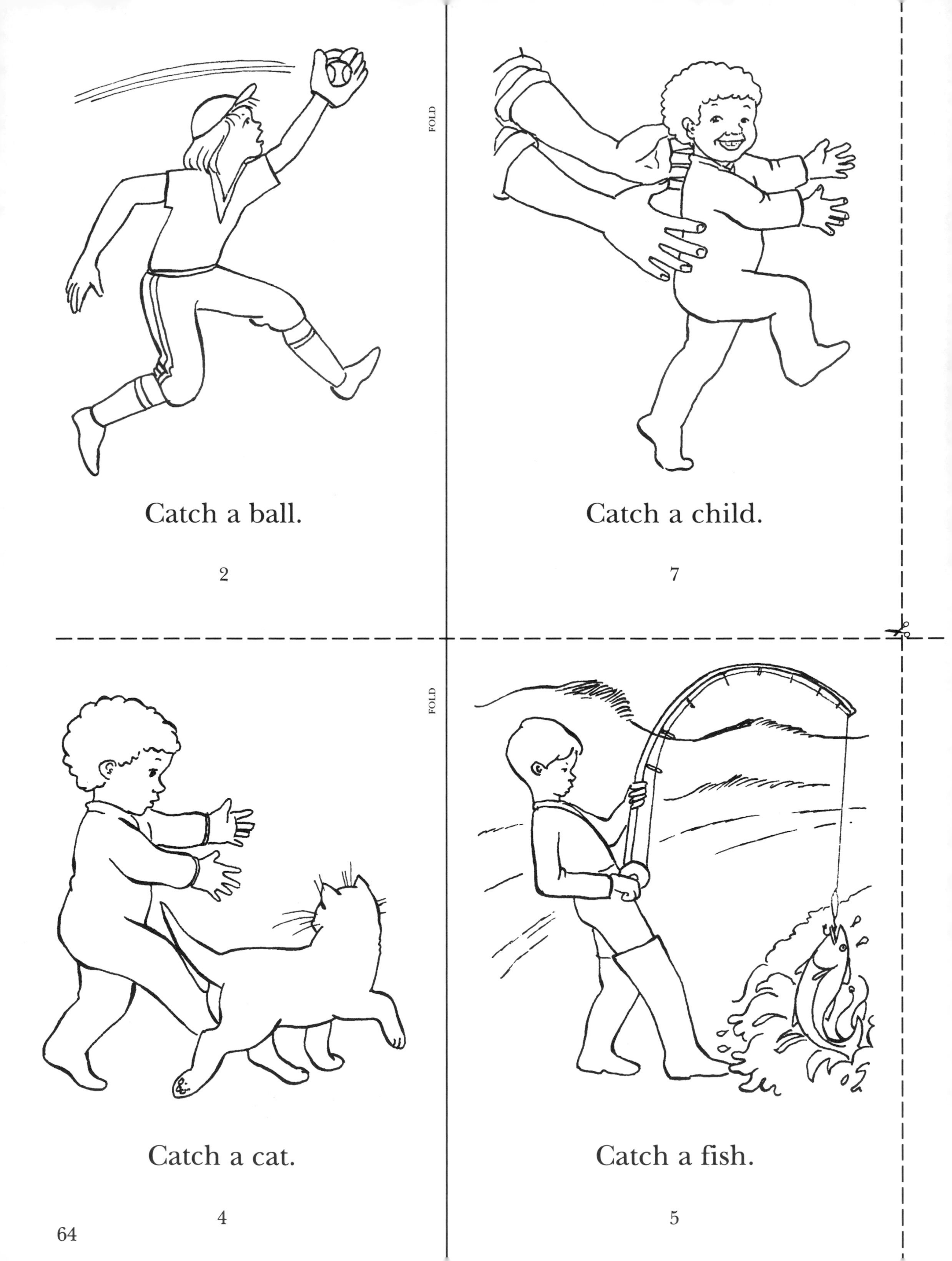
FOLD
Catch a ball.
2
Catch a child.
7
FOLD
Catch a cat.
4
Catch a fish.
5

I want to sing in
a band when I grow up.
What do you want to do?

When I grow
up, I want to

Hi! We are reading about two or more consonants together . . .
. . . like this:
king and queen
tree stump
and this:
best friends
tooth brush
Let's look at all of these sound clues together.

Write:

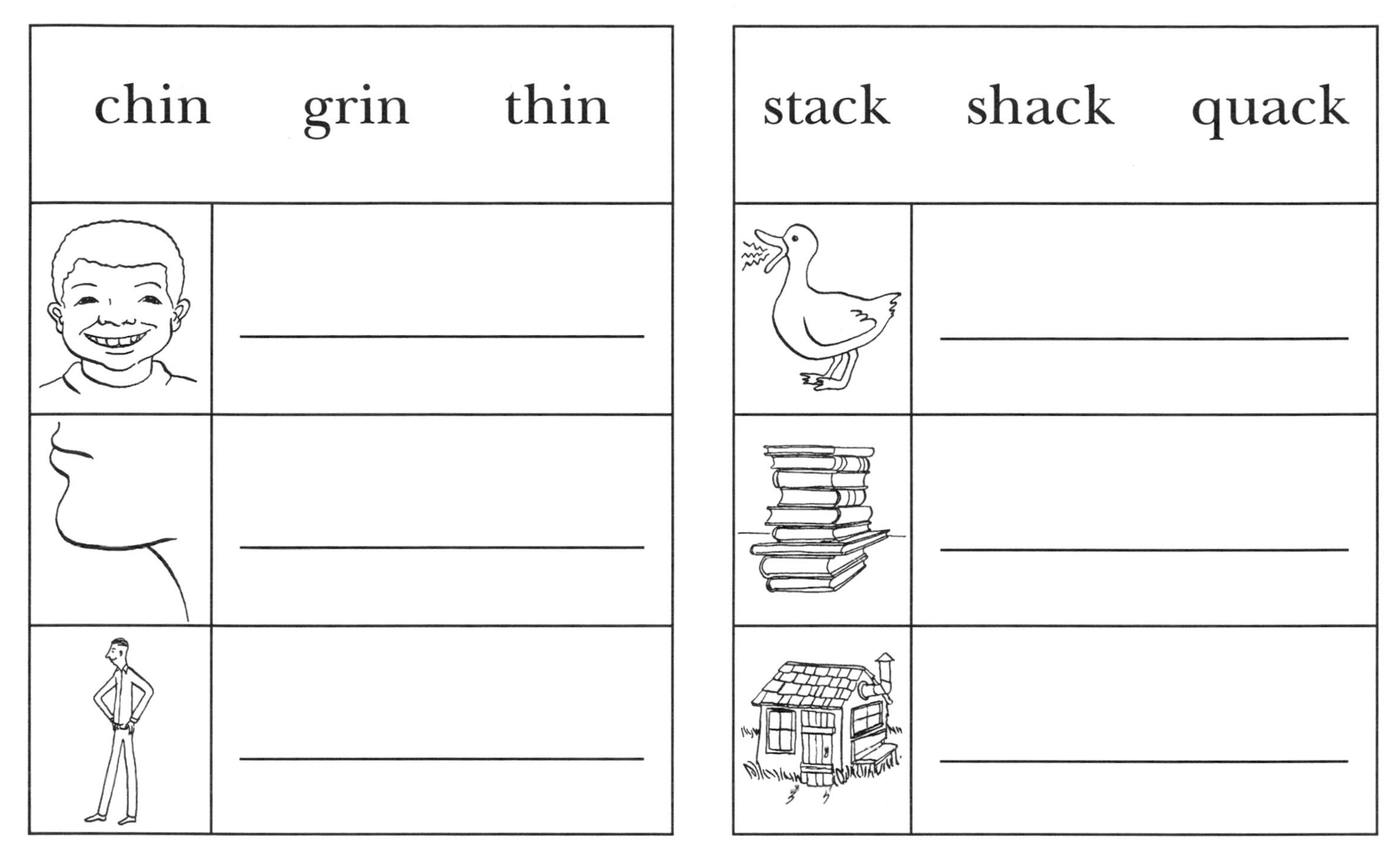

drum plum chum

trip flip ship

Write:

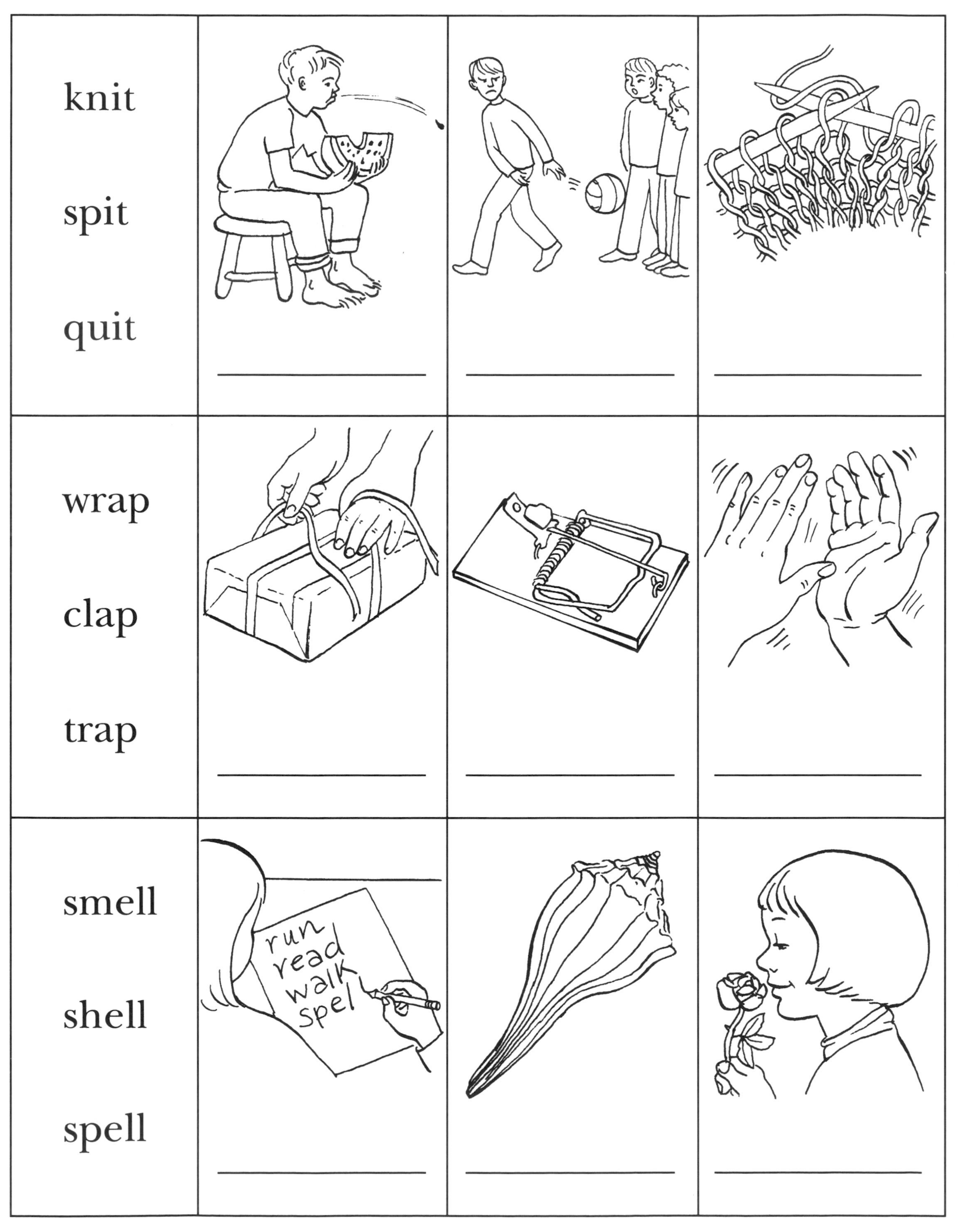
knit
spit
quit
wrap
clap
trap
smell
shell
spell
run
read
walk
spel

Write:

⬭ and write:

can't tan ask ant	still spell sled slip	clap clock black block
melt elm lent mend	clap strap wrap map	chimp bench bush bunch
trim went newt twin	felt sent fence fish	bulk bulb bull pulp
twins swell swim smell	help dell elk held	trip trap trick ripped
catch cash shack can't	gnat grit knit kilt	cash catch chat match

and write:

Match and write:

drinks

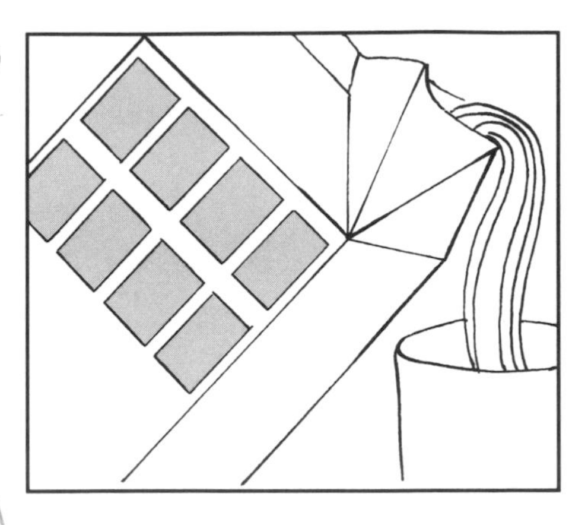

DUMP TRUCK

SKIM MILK

PLANTS

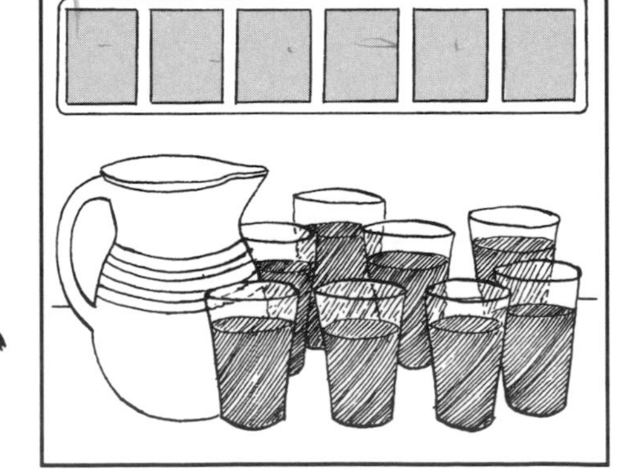

TRASH CANS

Use the words in the box. Fill in the blanks:

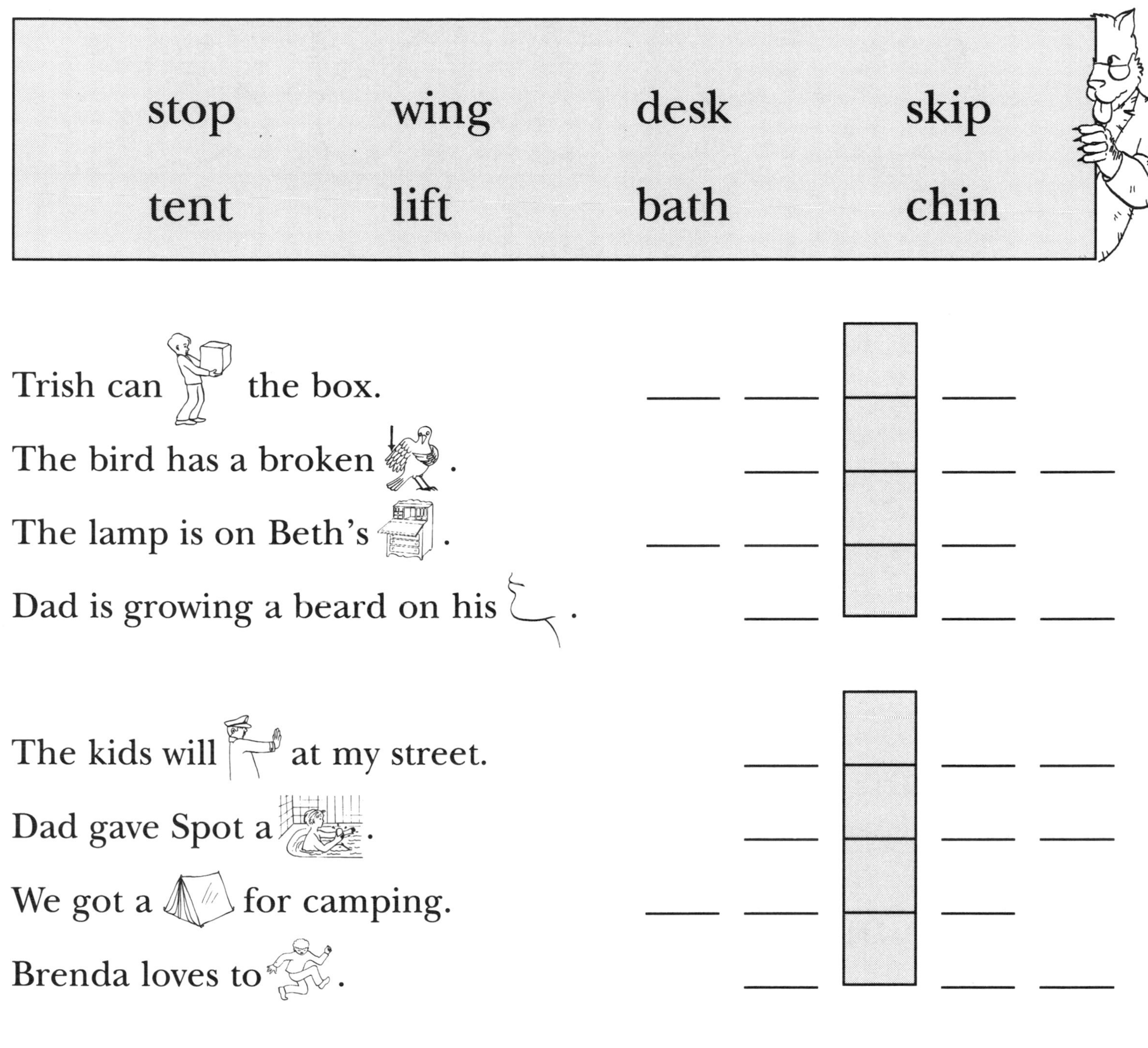

stop	wing	desk	skip
tent	lift	bath	chin

Trish can [picture] the box. ___ ___ [ ] ___

The bird has a broken [picture]. ___ [ ] ___ ___

The lamp is on Beth's [picture]. ___ ___ [ ] ___

Dad is growing a beard on his [picture]. ___ [ ] ___ ___

The kids will [picture] at my street. ___ [ ] ___ ___

Dad gave Spot a [picture]. ___ [ ] ___ ___

We got a [picture] for camping. ___ ___ [ ] ___

Brenda loves to [picture]. ___ [ ] ___ ___

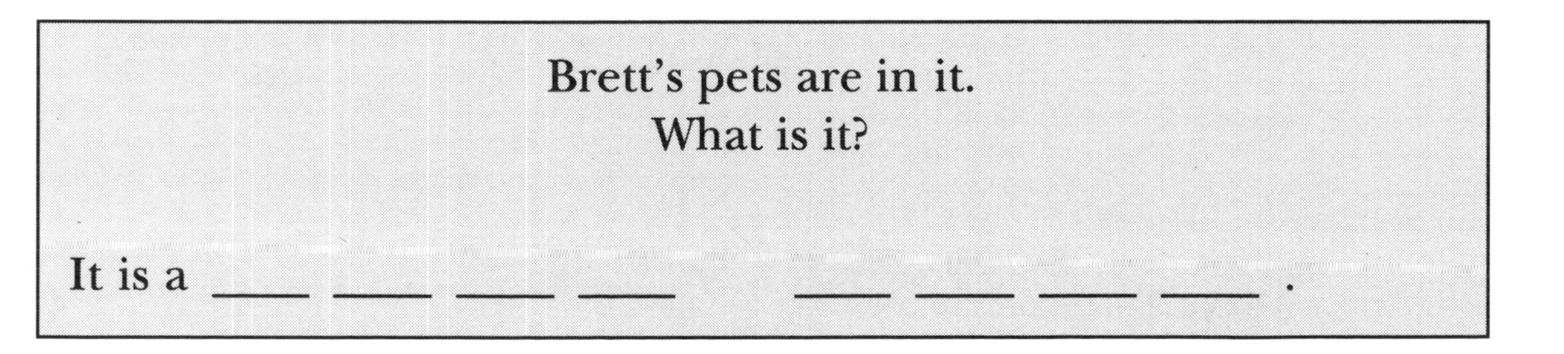

Brett's pets are in it.
What is it?

It is a ___ ___ ___ ___ ___ ___ ___ ___.

Write:

dress

sled

blocks

frog

lamb

pants

drum

black

vest

skunk

TOYS	
1	
2	
3	

CLOTHES	
1	
2	
3	

ANIMALS	
1	
2	
3	

X the one that does not belong:

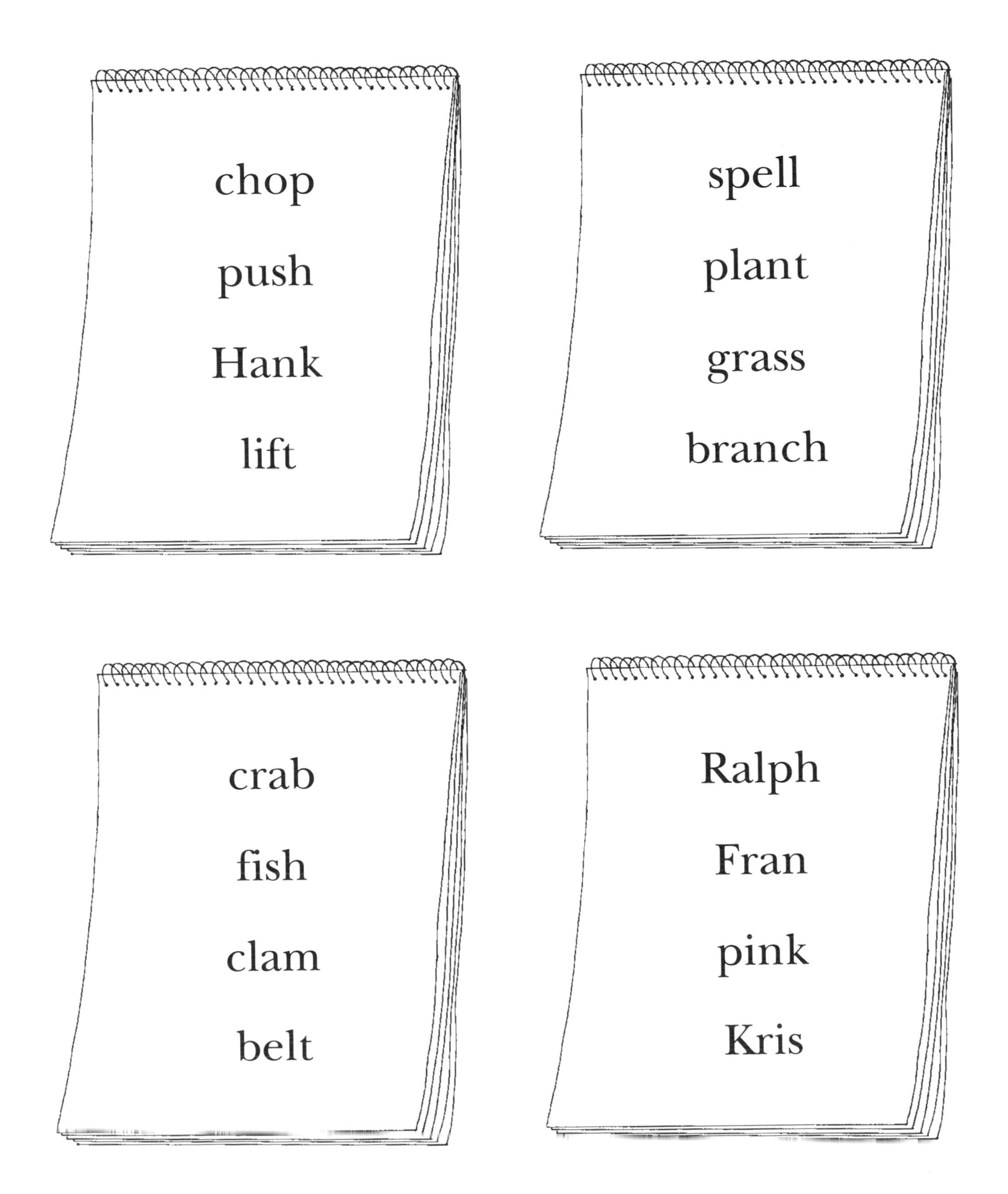

Think about the **sounds**. What word comes next?

flag	flip	flap	____________	dent
knit	knock	knot	____________	flat
went	lent	sent	____________	knob
ring	wing	king	____________	stop
				sing

Think about the **meanings**. What word comes next?

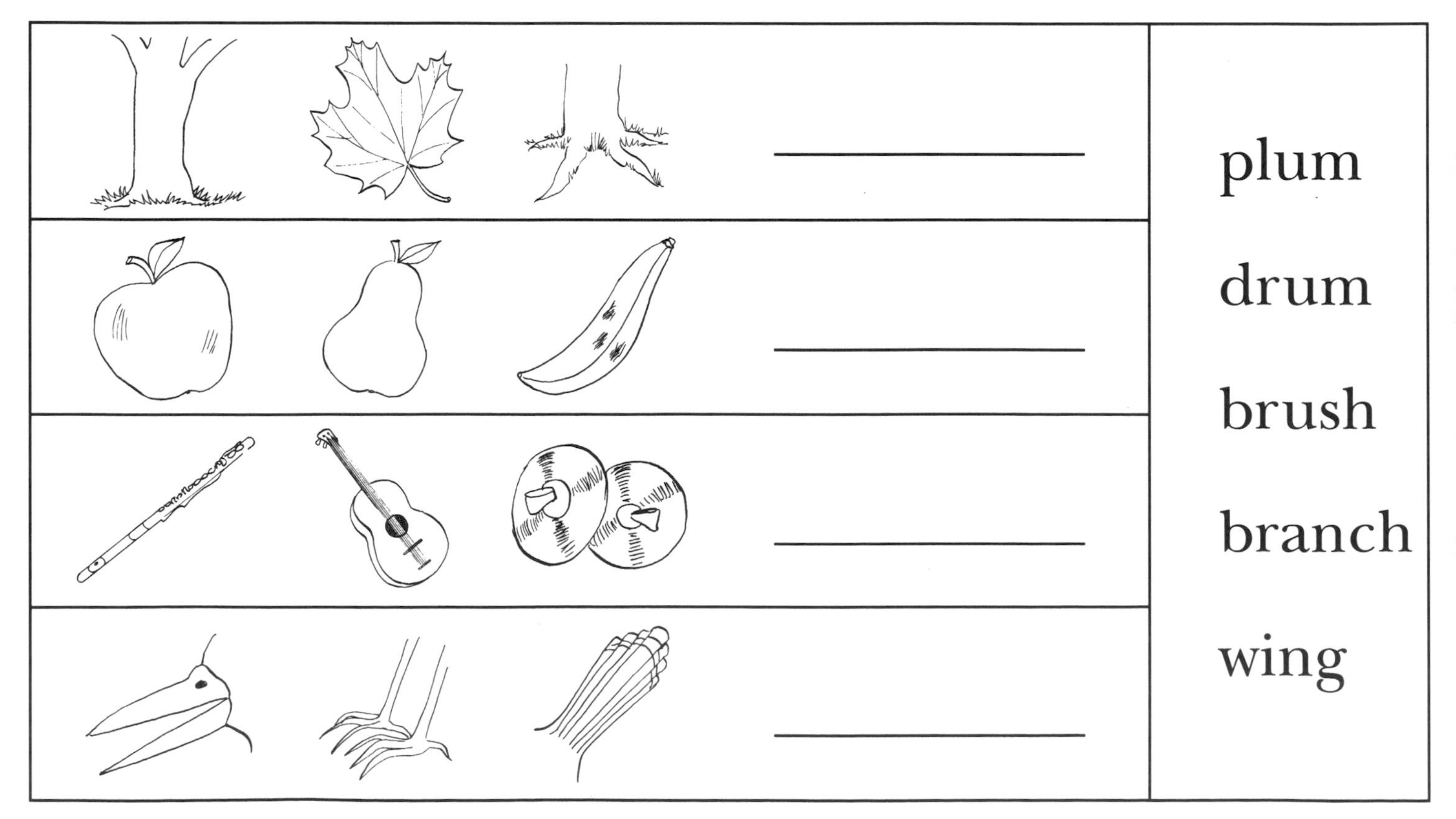

Where do these belong?
* = bonus word!

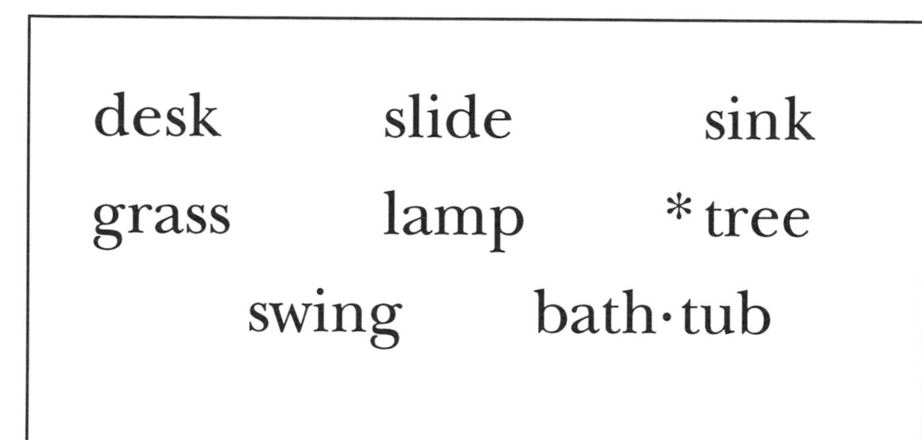

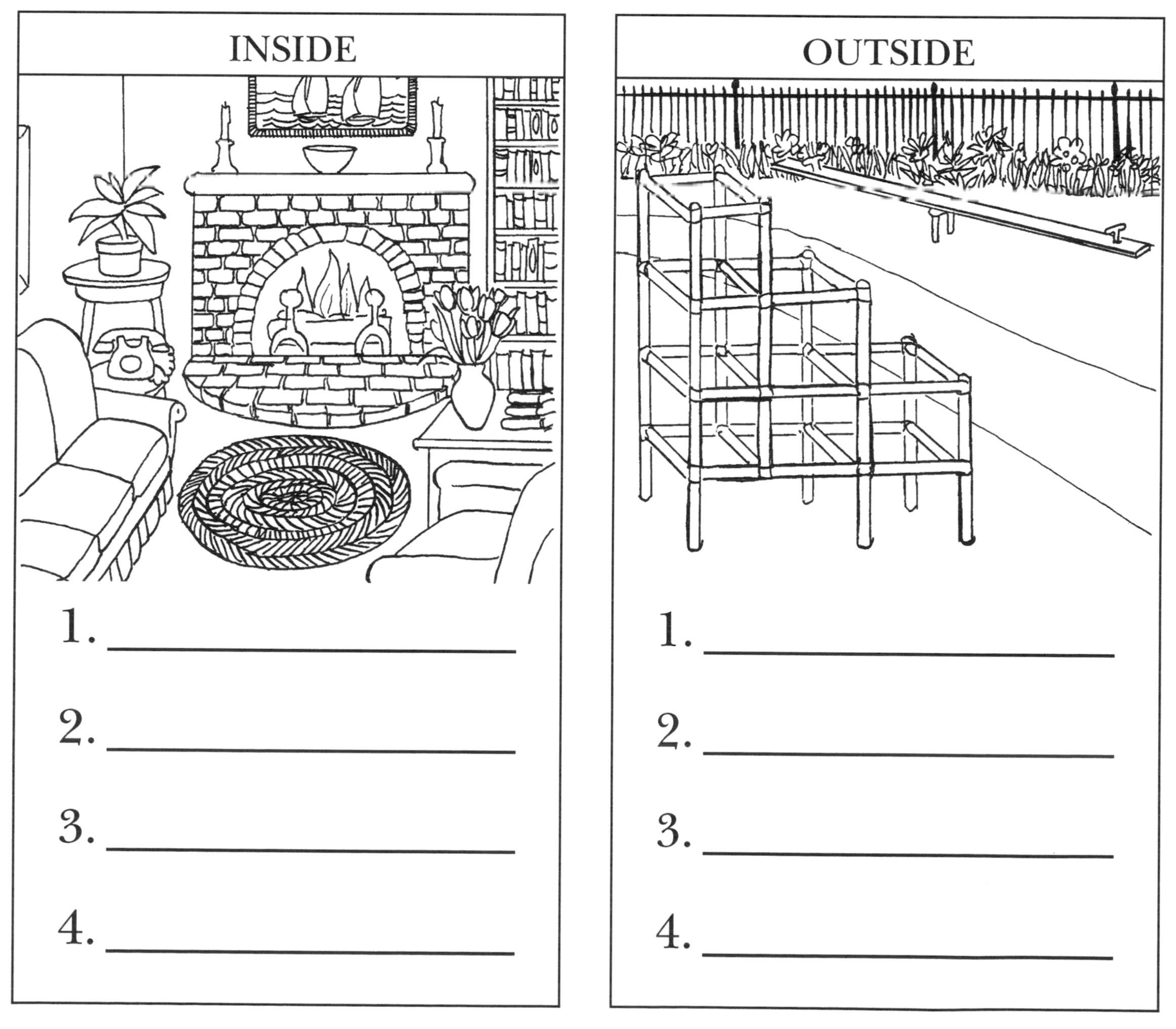

Write:

Chuck has ________ for a snack.

Brenda snacks on a ____________.

____________ snacks on French fries.

Beth chips plum milk Stan candy

Fran snacks on ____________.

____________ snacks on a pretzel.

Hank snacks on a ____________ shake.

What do you have for a snack?

I have ____________________________________

for a snack.

I'm scared of
skeletons.
What are you scared of?
I'm scared of

Dear Frank, July 1

I am sending you a box with a gift in it. I hope you can use it. Are you having fun at camp?

Love,
Gran

Help Frank write a thank-you note to Gran.
Use the words in the box.

things	Gran	slept	swim	Thanks

Jessica Saleedo

July 10

Dear Gran,

Thanks for the knapsack. I can carry my things in it. Last week we slept in a tent. I can swim too.

Love,
Frank

finish page

Write:

Cut on dotted lines and fold on solid line. Put together to form booklet. Staple and color.
They all skedaddle!
8
FOLD
Skedaddle!
1
The child skips.
6
FOLD
The chick scratches.
3

The frog splashes.

2

The skunk sprays!

7

The swan swims.

4

The snake slithers.

5

Cut on dotted lines and fold on solid line. Put together to form booklet. Staple and color.

and lands on ______________.

8

FOLD

Stepping

by

____

1

FOLD

The ______________ sprints.

6

The ______________ skips.

3

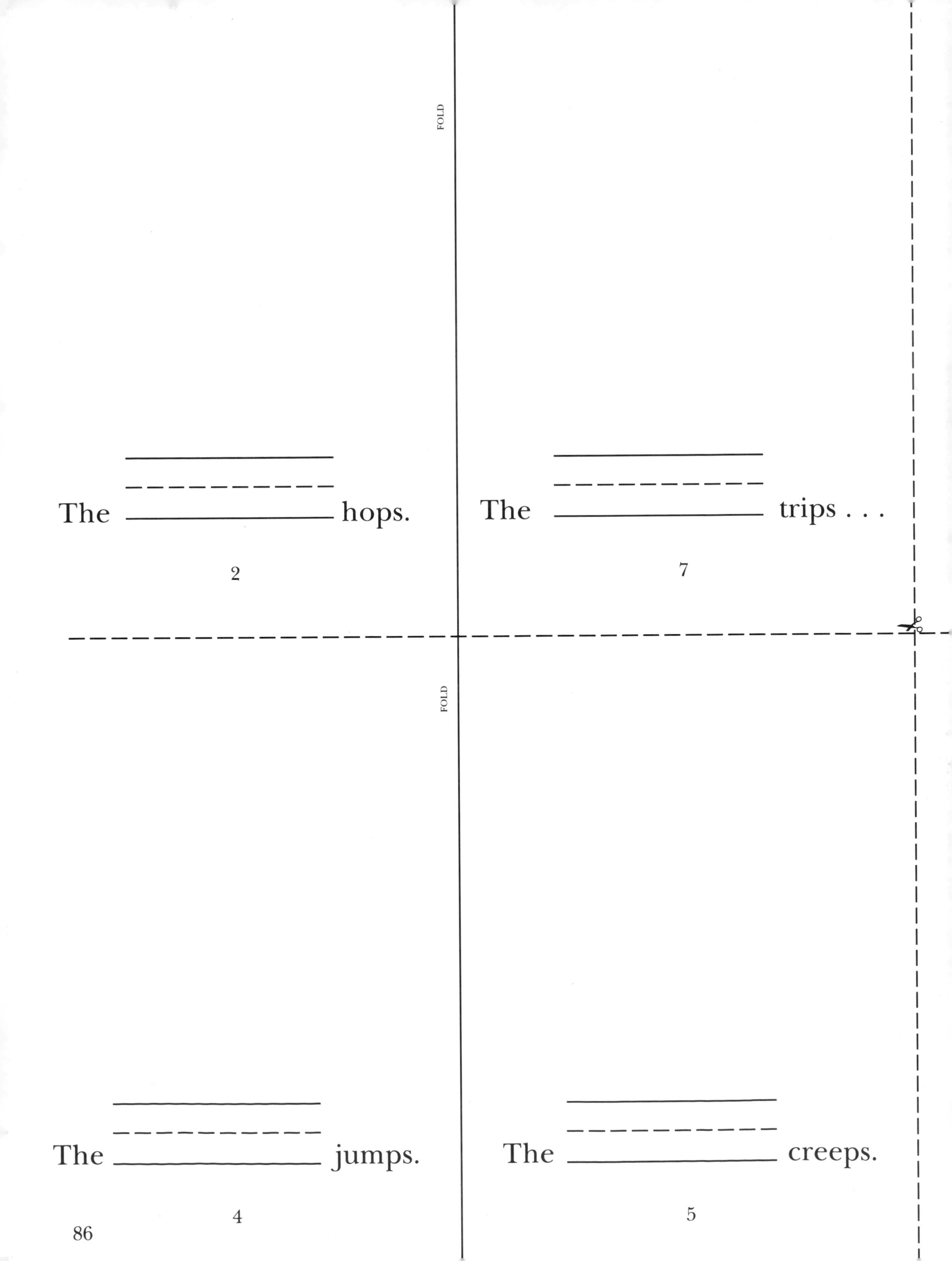
FOLD
The hops.
2
The trips . . .
7
FOLD
The jumps.
4
The creeps.
5